W. K. KELLOGG FOUNDATION

W. K. KELLOGG

W. K. KELLOGG FOUNDATION

THE FIRST ELEVEN YEARS

1930-1941

1942

BATTLE CREEK, MICHIGAN

PUBLISHED BY THE TRUSTEES OF THE W. K. KELLOGG FOUNDATION

PRINTED IN THE UNITED STATES OF AMERICA

THE LAKESIDE PRESS, R. R. DONNELLEY & SONS COMPANY, CHICAGO

W. K. KELLOGG FOUNDATION

W. K. KELLOGG FOUNDATION

PROFESSIONAL STAFF

GEORGE B. DARLING, DR. P.H.
President

EMORY W. MORRIS, D.D.S.
General Director

MATHEW R. KINDE, M.D.
Field Director

HERBERT H. HASSON, B.S.
Engineering Director

HUGH H. MASTERS, M.A.
Camp Director

HENRY J. OTTO, PH.D.
School Consultant

GRAHAM DAVIS
Hospital Consultant

MARGERITE WALES, M.A., R.N.
Nursing Consultant

ZOE WRIGHT, B.S.L.
Librarian

SPECIAL CONSULTANTS

JOHN E. GORDON, M.D. . . . . . . *Epidemiology*

GRANT FLEMING, M.D. . . . . *Preventive Medicine*

WILLIAM S. SADLER, M.D. . . . . . *Psychiatry*

WILSON G. SMILLIE, M.D. . . . . *Public Health*

CYRUS C. STURGIS, M.D. . . . . . *Medicine*

FOREWORD

THE first ten years of our effort to develop plans and formulate programs designed to help people to help themselves have taught all of us associated with the Foundation's activities that the basic principles of democracy are fundamental to successful cooperative community enterprises. There is sufficient evidence to indicate that many of the projects initiated by the Foundation during this period have assisted the people of numerous localities in working out practical solutions for many of their community problems. These Foundation programs have been directed towards improvement of the health, happiness, and well-being of children of this and future generations. In all of our work we have had in mind the possibility of utilizing our experience as a means of assisting other communities throughout the country in their efforts at self-improvement.

Our major concern has been to develop those programs which would contribute the greatest good to the largest number. While food, raiment, and shelter are necessities, and while it is essential that the educational facilities be maintained on high levels, it is only through cooperative planning, intelligent study, and group action—activities on the part of the entire community—that lasting results can be achieved.

The conception of the Foundation's plan of ministration on the co-operative problem-solving basis was largely due to the genius of the Foundation's President and General Director, Dr. Stuart Pritchard, who died August 4, 1940. In this connection, I wish to acknowledge the Foundation's indebtedness to Dr. Pritchard. My admiration for him could scarcely be better expressed than in the following words from the citation for the honorary degree of Doctor of Science conferred on him by the University of Michigan six weeks before his death: "He inspires and directs organized efforts to heal the hurts of mankind and to create a better environment for the growth of a wiser, healthier democracy. Under his guidance dream and vision become effective reality."

It is fortunate that Dr. Pritchard and his associates had proceeded far enough with the definition of the Foundation's aims and the formulation of its policies so that the programs which were started during the first decade can be carried on uninterruptedly by his associates. I am confident that under the Foundation's new leadership its work will continue to expand on many fronts during future years in the same spirit of helpfulness and in the same effective manner as under his direction and leadership.

It has given me a great deal of satisfaction to feel that the contributions of the Foundation will help children everywhere to face the future more confidently, healthier in mind and body, and more secure in their trust of this country and its institutions.

W. K. Kellogg

Gull Lake, Michigan,
October 15, 1941.

STUART PRITCHARD, M.D., D.Sc.

President & General Director of the W. K. Kellogg Foundation

August 4, 1940

Stuart Pritchard · Doctor of Science

A graduate of the University of Toronto, in charge of an important division of the Battle Creek Sanitarium from 1913 to 1930, and since then President and General Director of the W. K. Kellogg Foundation. A scientist of the highest attainments, a pioneer in the diagnosis and treatment of pulmonary diseases, a leader in promoting public health, endowed with independence, courage, and the knowledge of social needs. He inspires and directs organized efforts to heal the hurts of humankind, and to create a better environment for the growth of a wiser, healthier democracy. Under his guidance, dream and vision become effective reality.

. . .

Citation by Professor John G. Winter
Commencement Exercises, University of Michigan
June 15, 1940

CONTENTS

EXECUTIVE OFFICES

TO THE MEMBERS AND TRUSTEES
W. K. KELLOGG FOUNDATION:

Your officers submit herewith a report summarizing the first eleven years of the W. K. Kellogg Foundation, the last year of which has been under our joint direction.

The nation is now at war. Many of the programs outlined briefly herein were important in peace time, but they take on a new significance when half our national income and energy must be devoted to the war effort.

Effective health conservation programs which involve efficient operation of health departments, medical, dental, hospital, diagnostic laboratory, nursing, and sanitation facilities at a reasonable cost assume new importance as more and more physicians, dentists and nurses are drawn off to the armed forces and those who are left have more to do and less to do it with. Opportunities for the training of leaders must be preserved. Schools must meet their new obligations and opportunities in a larger measure than they have in the past.

Some construction will be important for key units, but most schools and hospitals must continue to use their present buildings. However, time as well as material must be conserved. Waste is equivalent to sabotage. It becomes the duty of all community agencies to bring essential programs to peak performance, to modernize facilities when necessary, and to operate with utmost efficiency.

The maximum utilization of community resources through cooperative effort in the solution of common health and educational problems has been the major interest of the Foundation. Such programs are today more than ever essential for national security. Your officers and staff have enjoyed working shoulder to shoulder with community leaders in these fields for many years. We are looking forward to the challenge of the years ahead with confidence. We hope that the Foundation's past experience, and the expansion program now under way, will permit it to play a useful role in helping to meet some of the problems that lie before us all.

Sincerely,

GEORGE B. DARLING, *President*
EMORY W. MORRIS, *General Director*

December 15, 1941

INTRODUCTION

THE principles of American democracy were early inculcated into the ideals of W. K. Kellogg, the seventh son of John Preston Kellogg, who in 1834 migrated with his family from Massachusetts to Michigan, traveling by horse and wagon and the Erie Canal. John Preston Kellogg established his first home on 300 acres of government timberland near what was then known as the Dickinson Settlement, 60 miles northwest of Detroit.

Ann J. Kellogg, the mother of W. K. Kellogg, was a native of western New York. Before her marriage to John Preston Kellogg, she was a school teacher, and at an early age she rode horseback through a dense forest to teach in her one-room log schoolhouse. She early realized that the maintenance of that freedom and liberty for which these early pioneers had made so many sacrifices depended upon the development and fostering of adequate educational facilities for the rising generation of the new American democracy.

In 1854 John Preston Kellogg moved to Jackson, Michigan, where he began the manufacture of brooms. Two years later he moved to Battle Creek, where, on April 7, 1860, W. K. Kellogg was born. Following an uneventful childhood which was more or less typical for a youngster of that day and in such a pioneer environment, he attended school and learned the broommaking trade, working with his father throughout his youth. At eighteen he went to Texas, taking over the management of a broom factory.

A year later he returned to Michigan, and, after the completion of a business course, became associated with the Battle Creek Sanitarium on April 1, 1880. For twenty-five years he assumed many responsibilities connected with the business management and financial direction of that institution.

At the age of forty-six he organized a company to manufacture and merchandise the first prepared breakfast food to bear his name. A few years after the establishment of this business, in a letter written to an acquaintance, he gave expression to his desire and intention, in case his business ventures should prosper, to devote some of his means to social welfare.

Even at this early date he had begun to formulate in his mind the concept of contributing to the advancement of human welfare by some method which would help people to help themselves—which would give them practical assistance in solving their own problems. And this idea of encouraging the development of a strong and self-reliant citizenship became the guiding principle of all the subsequent policies of the Foundation.

As Mr. Kellogg prospered and was able to increase the number of his contributions to worthy causes, he decided that he should provide some systematic and businesslike method of administering these benefactions. In 1925 he established the Fellowship Corporation, which served for the next five years as the agency through which many of his helpful endeavors were directed. His major contributions through this period included a grant for the Agricultural School at Augusta, Michigan; the W. K. Kellogg Bird Sanctuary, the Kellogg experimental farms, and a reforestation project, which were later given to the Michigan State College of East Lansing. Gifts in Battle Creek included the Associated Boys' Club Building (Youth Building), the Altrusa Day Nursery, the City Market, land for a Boy Scout camp, and a grant for more than half the cost of the Ann J. Kellogg School. Numerous contributions were also made for student scholarships and for research in various fields. The Kellogg Radiation Laboratory at the California Institute of Technology, Pasadena, California, was established during this period.

In June 1930 Mr. Kellogg established the W. K. Kellogg Foundation, whose charter provided for the formulation of a comprehensive and well-organized undertaking to improve the health, happiness, and well-being of mankind—especially children.

W. K. KELLOGG FOUNDATION

THE FIRST ELEVEN YEARS OF THE W. K. KELLOGG FOUNDATION

THE STORY OF A COOPERATIVE ENTERPRISE

THE Charter* of the Foundation sets forth its purpose as "the promotion of the health, education, and welfare of mankind, but principally of children and youth, directly or indirectly."

The first problem which the Trustees faced was the selection of a plan of action whereby this purpose could be forwarded.

A preliminary review was first undertaken of the activities of other Foundations in this field. Then, proceeding on the principle that problem solving should begin at home, a study was made of the rural area around Battle Creek. This study pointed out in dramatic fashion the wide discrepancy existing between what is known and what is practiced in the fields of health, education, welfare, and recreation.

The problem

All the components of an average northern white rural community are present in the area surrounding Battle Creek. These communities are typically rural and possess a little better than average economic resources. They have active and interested community leaders. They have the usual quota of physicians, dentists, school teachers, and all the other human resources. Notwithstanding all of this, health programs were practically non-existent, many schools were neglected and inadequate, and community facilities, such as hospitals and libraries, were often either absent or of poor quality. In these respects the situation was no different from that to be found in thousands of other communities throughout the United States. The distressing thing was that no better use was being made of the opportunities afforded by the American system to provide really adequate answers to these challenging community needs.

*See Appendix "B"

Policy adopted

As a result of the study of the programs of major foundations and the consideration of these problems at national and local levels, the Foundation's Board of Trustees came to its first major decision. The Foundation would use its resources mainly in the application of knowledge rather than in research or relief. Research is of unquestioned value but support was already available for many worth-while projects. Relief is necessary but has come to be an accepted responsibility of government. Nothing seemed quite so important as finding ways and means to help the average citizen apply the knowledge that had already been won for him.

The Foundation became interested, then, not in providing service for the people of impoverished areas, but in ways and means to help those with average resources to better achieve some of the community programs made possible by an effective combination of scientific knowledge and cooperative teamwork under the democratic system.

Specific objectives

For its goal it chose the objectives set forth so clearly and completely in the Children's Charter of the White House Conference on Child Health and Protection.* For its field of immediate endeavor it chose its own neighborhood, the rural area immediately surrounding Battle Creek.

The needs of the rural child are greater than those of the city child today. This reversal of the old order has been brought about because the cities for self-preservation had to develop compensatory services to protect their inhabitants and promote their health, education and welfare. Philanthropy has made many contributions to urban life and to colleges and universities. Less has been done for the country child.

With a field of interest chosen and the locale selected, the next question was obviously one of method. How could the Foundation best help these people to help themselves?

Responsibility remains with the people

The health and welfare of the children in the area in which the Foundation was interested were the responsibilities of the men and women in that area. The Foundation's mission was to help them, not to substitute

*See Appendix "D"

for them. It could not set right all the complex ills of the social structure; it had no mandate to attempt such a task. It had no cure-all to offer. The Foundation felt that this was neither the time nor the place for demonstrations by experts of programs for the less well-informed to follow.

By what right did the Foundation approach these people and with what kind of assistance? Teamwork and cooperation with emphasis on individual initiative is a typically American procedure. It is common practice in a democracy for the group with a problem, the group with an idea for its solution, the group with technical skill, the group with labor, and the group with capital to get together in a cooperative, mutually helpful enterprise. The Foundation could provide funds for cooperative community programs of a social character, just as banks provide concentration of funds for business enterprises.

Money is a means not a method

Capital, however, is only a part of the total picture. In the health and welfare field, as in business, success or failure is determined, not by how much money is invested, but by how well the members of the team carry out their respective jobs.

Then if this money was to be made to serve human needs effectively it must be spent in such a way as to help those leaders who are really trying to work out answers to the social problems of their communities.

People not systems

This emphasis on people seemed important to the Foundation. The Trustees put their faith in people and not in systems. When a program is not working well it is a common mistake to look for the trouble in the system rather than in the people. The real problem is more often with the individuals than with the plan. When it is, a change in the system is of little help. The same people are involved. They have the same knowledge and attitudes under the new system as under the old. Education seemed to be the answer.

Adults can be educated

The Trustees decided to turn their backs upon systems either old or new and to invest in people. This decision brought them face to face with a curious though common belief that adults are incapable of further learning. The only thing to do, they were told, was to incorporate the proper attitude in the education of the young physician in the medical school, the young dentist, the young teacher, the young farmer and then hope that in the course of the next generation they would bring about the improvements so easily obtained with the proper leadership.

Experience failed to bear out these pessimistic generalizations. Local professional and lay people concerned with social conditions had definite ideas as to what the problems were and what they wanted to do about them. They were more or less alive to their responsibilities and were equally cognizant of their deficiencies in training to meet their community obligations. The Trustees came to their next important decision.

Problems are where you find them

The place to begin was with the problems that the people recognized rather than with those that someone thought they ought to see. Any assistance the Foundation could offer should not be designed to promote a preconceived plan but to bring to the communities through their own leaders the best of current thought in order that those directly concerned could work out their own solutions. The challenge, of course, was to see whether local leadership, so stimulated, could develop really effective methods to meet community needs and thus advance the cause of child health, education, and welfare.

Experience must be exchanged

A method was needed by which these people could study their problems, learn to appreciate the wealth of their resources, exchange experience, talk with others who had solved similar problems successfully, and find their own answers through cooperative community action. This meant an adult education program for all of the people in the community who had anything to do with health, education, recreation or welfare. This is an astonishingly complex matter.

How opinions are formed

There is no one way by which a person forms his opinion on a given subject. For example, a study of a child's attitude toward pasteurized milk in a rural school shows clearly that the attitudes and the opinions of many individuals are involved. The school teacher, the school board, the local physician, the dairyman, the veterinarian, the milk plant owner, the local service club, the neighbor, the dentist, the newspaper, the magazines, the radio, motion pictures, advertisements, the camp to which the child goes, his church, the opinions of his parents and of other children—all these factors and many more have a bearing on his attitude toward milk and on whether or not the milk used in the school shall be pasteurized or raw.

Plans for adult education must take into consideration the multiplicity of these forces, the variation in their direction and intensity, and the fact that they sometimes supplement one another, sometimes conflict. A well-designed program of or for any of these groups may be thwarted by indifference or opposition of one or more of the others.

Leaders provide the key

A problem as complicated as this can be approached effectively only by breaking it down into its component parts. Each of these parts can then be attacked separately, but a coordinated plan is necessary so that the individual programs will reinforce each other and ultimately bring about a unified community attitude. The importance of the role of the accepted or undiscovered leaders of the community is clear. Recognition of this fact led the Foundation to adopt the principle that adult education should work with and through the leaders. Programs of mass education that fail to allow for the proper preparation and participation of the communities' accepted leaders inevitably result in open conflict and sometimes in more or less complete disruption of community life.

The community is the unit

This intra-relation of various people and their opinions made it obvious that it would not be effective to concentrate an adult education program on one group in a community, either professional or lay. The unit for such a project must necessarily be the community itself. So it became clear that the initial area should not be too large. The choice of a rural field was again reinforced by the importance of keeping these community relationships as simple as possible.

If the first problem, then, was the education of community leaders, how was this to be accomplished? The answer was not simple. Different approaches had to be formulated for the various professional groups, and still other plans had to be perfected for reaching numerous lay groups either organized or unorganized.

New methods needed

More effective methods are needed than now exist for a rapid exchange of human experience between individuals working with the same problems. It is at this point that the greatest opportunity exists to reduce the tremendous loss the race now suffers in its attempts to pass on from one generation to the next the knowledge and experience won at such great cost.

One of the major incongruities of present day civilization is that our entire educational allowance of energy and money is spent on the training of the young, without giving adequate thought or support to the equally productive field of adult education.

Problem-solving clinics

A visitor from a remote corner of the globe might logically expect to find included in our cultural centers, great problem-solving clinics where men and women who have had some degree of success in dealing with actual problems lead discussions designed to help others to arrive at better solutions of their own. Actually, most of the extension courses of the universities, their workshops, and summer courses are intended primarily to further prepare the student for advanced degrees, rather than to help him with the job he has to do from day to day. A method had to be found for the great educational centers to provide postgraduate and continuing education for their graduates that would deal with practical problems in a practical way.

Problem identification

The place to begin was with accepted problems, but the great discrepancy between the problems recognized by the local leaders and those listed by experienced students of the social structure could not be ignored. It was obvious that both were real and important. It was apparent that some machinery was needed to bring the larger problems into focus at the local level. Furthermore, the factors had to be reduced to simple terms within the personal experience of the people before they could take on real meaning for those who might want to do something about them.

The whole social and economic structure of the country is changing. Ways and means of meeting the cost of professional services have to be considered as a part of this picture. No master plans so far proposed—various forms of state medicine, group practice, sickness insurance and the like—seem satisfactory. Master plans in general must have extraordinary flexibility to permit adaptation to the many and markedly different local situations.

Cooperation depends on understanding

Ultimately a working solution must come from within the ranks of the professions concerned. Certainly satisfactory solutions cannot be arrived at without their sympathetic understanding and active cooperation. It is important that these professions have opportunities to get first-hand experience with the problems in their respective fields by active participation in cooperative programs. It is obvious that constant and painstaking analysis is required and that the responsibility for control should remain with the professional societies.

Medical societies, after all, are simply associations of men with individual practices. Boards of supervisors are only groups of men who represent individual townships. Dentists are primarily concerned with their own private practices, not with the lack of dental service for children generally. All of these men needed to discover at first hand the significance of the problems in their own field in their own communities. How could this best be done?

Organization is important

The first requisite in a program involving the cooperation of individuals is organization. Some professions were well organized, others only nominally, and some not at all. The first step was to help these professional and lay groups to organize themselves into effective societies so that local leadership would have effective channels for expression, and so that responsibility could be accepted.

But teamwork does not result automatically from the formation of an organization. Individuals can function effectively only after they have learned to regard common problems as a challenge to their ability to cooperate rather than as opportunities for competitive action. Community programs require group action. Group action calls for a common purpose and agreement as to method. Free discussion is important but someone has to take the initiative if results are to be obtained.

Health departments necessary

A health department potentially provides the most effective machinery for discovering and properly evaluating the relative significance of various health problems and of organizing programs for their solution. However, few believe that a completely satisfactory pattern for local health department service has, as yet, been established. The lack of enthusiastic support the country over seems to give more or less direct evidence that these departments are not meeting local needs as well as they should.

Child health work in many of the public health programs in the country seems to have reached the point of diminishing returns. The emphasis in school work, for example, has changed from a program to detect communicable disease in school children, through the stage of examination for physical defects, to the promotion of health. Depending upon the ability and opportunity of the workers in this field, elaborate and expensive machinery has been built up to accomplish these specified results. Scores of school physicians inspect children for physical defects. Corps of public health nurses make home calls in an attempt to convince parents of the desirability of having these defects corrected. This is backed up with health education, news releases, radio, advertising—all designed to correct conditions that should never have been allowed to develop.

It is difficult, if not impossible, to instill in the minds of parents confidence in an impersonal organization in matters concerning the health of their children. What has actually taken place in many communities is a transfer of confidence from the physician to confidence in the school nurse. Parents rarely see the school physician. He sees the child for only a few moments. He has no previous knowledge of the child's history and family background, except what he can get from the official record or can secure in the brief time available.

The results obtained with this machinery are disappointing and the little that is accomplished is achieved at a disproportionate cost.

Defects do not occur spontaneously. They are related directly to the development of the individual over a considerable period of time. Many found in school children develop in the preschool period. The present machinery of the school system cannot be expected to produce results with the preschool child. Consideration must be given to the importance of establishing early a proper relationship between the patient, his family and their physician for continuous medical supervision. The desired results can be achieved in no other way.

Improved distribution of effort

It seemed that if a fraction of the time, energy and money that is spent on these ineffective methods could be spent in educating the child and his parent to consult the family physician about all health matters, and in the preparation of the physician for this opportunity, a really forward-looking program with increasing effectiveness at a progressively decreasing cost to the public could be obtained.

Prevention implies education

It was recognized that if the physicians and dentists were to take their proper place in such a movement, they had to become educators as well. Experience has shown that the hairline distinction commonly drawn between preventive and curative medicine is entirely unjustified. Both are important parts of medical practice and should be carried out in the offices of the physicians and in the homes of the patients. But it is true that curative medicine and reparative dentistry do not need the educational technique that preventive medicine and dentistry demand. No education is needed to get a person with a toothache to a dentist's office. Unfortunately it is too late to immunize a child after he has symptoms of the disease.

Professions challenged

This was the challenge to the professions. The simple suggestion of a physician who has the confidence of a family whose mother he has served at childbirth that "Of course, Johnnie will be immunized against diphtheria on his ninth month's birthday" should be worth more than any amount of education, direct or indirect, through the radio, the printing presses, talks to the P.T.A., or the well-intentioned advice of the public health nurse.

If, then, the chief difference between the preventive and curative program lies in the educational factor, why should the physician or dentist not do the educating simply and directly—with profit not only to the patient, but to himself. A strong community educational program including health education in the schools and the important family case work of the public health nurses would then reinforce their activities instead of conflicting with them.

Agency required

Nevertheless, no program can be carried out unless there is a strong coordinating organization interested in solving all of the community's health problems. The ideal health department would be such an organization. Perhaps what was needed was a health department where new methods could be worked out for the solution of these problems without undue regard for established patterns.

It so happened that none of the counties immediately surrounding Battle Creek had county health departments.

Barry County had an opportunity to qualify for aid in establishing a health department. The state health department and the county supervisors asked the W. K. Kellogg Foundation to supplement their funds to make such a department possible. A year later another county, and then another, requested assistance from the Foundation to make health departments possible.

Financial problems

The problem of finding adequate financial support for health departments, even when the service fits community needs and is demanded by the public, is as difficult in rural Michigan as it is in other country districts of the United States. County governments whose only source of income is the personal and property tax find it impossible to meet the entire cost of modern health service. Rural citizens contribute their share to state and federal taxes. Substantial funds must be made available from both state and federal sources if the advantages of this service are to be available to rural children. Although Michigan law provides for a state subsidy of 25% of the cost of local health departments the upper limit of this contribution at the present time is set at $3,000.00 per county annually. Federal funds are available but these are also inadequate and are on a temporary basis. The problem facing local governing bodies is a real one.

The basis for cooperation

The Foundation was not interested in financing additional demonstrations of the value of health departments as such but it was willing to subsidize a few such units if the local leaders were interested in new types of community health programs, and were willing to invest some of their own money. It was recognized that for the type of work contemplated special staffs and unusual facilities would be needed. The counties interested in this project were to be under no obligation to take over the program intact. The construction of a modern highway requires the use of highly specialized engineers. Once the road is well built a simpler maintenance organization is sufficient to keep it going. The same may be true of health departments and their problem of social engineering. It was agreed that when adequate financial support became regularly available from state and federal sources the Foundation would withdraw its support except for special funds that might be granted in connection with university training programs and field fellowship activities. In the meantime the communities could draw upon the Foundation's resources in the study of their problems.

Return on investment

Nevertheless, the Trustees believed that the programs should be practical and that every dollar spent should return at least a dollar's worth of direct service to the children of the area. This meant that social and professional contributions as to method had to be dividends over and above the normal returns on the investment. Local children were to be the immediate beneficiaries of the service rendered. Children throughout the nation were to benefit if the way in which the service was rendered proved to have significance.

Seven counties selected

Seven rural counties were finally selected from among the many that applied. They were near enough to each other to permit effective use of consultants, joint staff meetings, easy exchange of experience, and to permit later on, their organization into a field training area. Several counties were needed so that similar problems could be attacked in different ways. Seven were chosen so as to provide a reasonably sized staff that could work as a group on the problems at hand. Counties were contiguous so that the various programs could reinforce each other, and so that a successful plan could spread by its own merit throughout the project.

THE PROGRAM BEGINS

When the counties were selected, Foundation grants were made to the boards of supervisors, health departments were established, and the program was under way.

Health departments

The staffs of these county health departments included a medical director, one or more public health engineers, one public health nurse for every 5,000 people, and clerks. The health department program included the collection of statistics on births, deaths, and disease; measures to control the outbreak and spread of communicable diseases; extensive and helpful work for expectant mothers, babies, preschool and school children; and complete programs in school hygiene, food and milk sanitation, and general sanitation. The health departments operate on a budget of $1.00 per capita. Of this amount the state contributes approximately 10c per capita, the counties 25c, the Foundation the rest.

All versus some

The health director, a well-qualified physician, has the same general responsibilities as have other health officers. He must have adequate programs of preventive medical service and children's dentistry. However, he develops these programs on a problem-solving basis using all the resources of the county. This means that programs are for *all* children including poor, and not, as too often the case, a service for the poor only carried out as a "demonstration."

It was recognized from the start that no county health department would ever have enough money to provide *for the entire population* the type of personal service offered a few by many of the health departments throughout the United States through clinics and direct service by salaried physicians and dentists. Consequently, these departments did not try to render such service even to a small part of the population, but rather concerned themselves with the development of community plans and programs which would ultimately bring about such services for all through the cooperation of the professions.

The middle ground

This has significance because of the two diametrically opposed philosophies prevalent in the United States. There are those who prefer the inadequacies and inequalities of the status quo to any organized or cooperative program because they fear a further loss of the democratic process of government if master plans are developed. Then there are many who see an extension of salaried physicians and dentists on the health department staffs in some form of state medicine as the only solution. This program provided a middle ground where cooperative solution of these problems might be obtained locally without government domination. If such a method could be made to work it might prove to be a significant contribution to American life.

Education versus compulsion

Educational procedure was to take precedence over legislative enactment and law enforcement. Laws are important when they define the opinion of the majority they directly concern. They are useful in dealing with the few who will not cooperate except under threat of compulsion. But the importance of the law in public health programs has been much over-emphasized. The adoption of an ordinance is often an educational procedure only to the governing council that discusses and debates the law,—even they are likely to learn more after the law is adopted than before!

MARSHALING RESOURCES

The staffs of the county health departments considered both personal service and environmental sanitation as community problems to be solved by organization of resources through a process of education and cooperative action. As a consequence, unusual plans and programs have been developed experimentally by these county health departments that lead to new horizons in public health practice.

The health departments, then, were committed to a policy of developing programs based on the active participation of the professions and community groups concerned. First they had to discover the nature and extent of the problems of their counties.

New tools

Some tools were already available but most of these were based on a comparison of local programs with a statistical average of current practices. There were no really acceptable criteria for the measurement of problems. New methods had to be developed experimentally. In a short time modern business record systems were adapted to their needs and the health problems of the communities were brought into focus.

These record systems proved to be an important step. Instead of simply tabulating services rendered, statistical methods were worked out to measure the degree of success achieved and the rate of change. The proportion of children under continuous medical supervision or receiving dental care is more important than the number of homes visited or pamphlets distributed. Figures were based on community units combined into districts served by individual members of the staff. This permitted objective measurement of experimental methods. Program planning and evaluation took on a new significance. The field worker had the personal satisfaction that comes from demonstrable accomplishment.

Knowledge is not understanding

Exact knowledge of the health situation was not enough. The problems were appreciated at that time only by the health department personnel. It then became necessary for the physicians, dentists, and other community professional leaders to understand them and appreciate their significance.

Professional organizations

The first step was, as already suggested, the organization of key professional and lay societies, and the discussion with them of the numerous community problems found.

These societies then created a number of advisory committees to cooperate with the health director and to coordinate their own manifold activities. As time went on, these committees provided their share of leadership in the extension of the programs. County health councils were ultimately formed but they were useful only when individuals on these councils could really reflect the considered opinions of their societies and not merely their personal points of view.

When physicians and dentists were confronted with the roles they were to play in the medical and dental programs, the professional men confessed frankly that they were in need of additional training if they were to do the kind of job they wanted to do. They asked for special postgraduate courses in preventive medicine and children's dentistry.

Postgraduate courses

This presented a new challenge to the Foundation's directors and consultants who became naturally the go-between for the community groups and the various cultural centers where such training might be expected to be provided. The dearth of any real facilities to bring postgraduate or continuing education to these groups on a problem-solving basis was brought out in dramatic fashion. Only the physicians had even a semblance of the facilities required. Nevertheless, interest and cooperation were finally secured and many courses of a new type were provided for physicians and dentists in educational institutions in different parts of the country. These courses were a judicious mixture of selected current problems and preparation for the newer preventive services.

But education without activity is a sterile thing. Real understanding could be obtained only through personal experience. However, this experience was required by the plan itself since professional service was to be provided only by the physicians and dentists already living in these communities.

LEARNING BY DOING

Following their postgraduate study, the members of the medical societies worked out with the health departments organized programs for the examination of the children in their communities. For the first time, through their joint experience, they had a picture of the needs of the community as a whole. Then programs for the correction of defects and control of communicable diseases were developed. Their plans called for payment for these services by the parents who could afford them and certification to the health departments by the physicians or dentists of those who could not. The health departments made contributions through funds granted by the Foundation toward the cost of the services rendered indigent children so that all could be included.

Law of supply and demand

The establishment of these funds raised the interesting question as to who should ultimately pay for these services. Three main factors were involved. First, there was the creation of a public demand for adequate health service and education. Second, the professions had to prepare themselves to provide this service. The third problem involved workable plans for meeting the cost, including that for the ever-present proportion who could not afford to pay for the service. The physicians and dentists were told that, if they were interested in seeing how far they could develop the demand—and the supply, the Foundation would meet the cost of the educational phase and would temporarily make a contribution toward the cost of those unable to pay. In the light of the experience thus obtained, the problem of the non-pay cases would then have to be dealt with through the proper funds from local, state, or federal sources. This was a responsibility that a private agency could not assume indefinitely.

New patterns

So plans were adopted and thousands of children began to go to the offices of the private practitioners. Within a short period of time the medical society meetings took on a new quality. Preventive medicine and its social and economic aspects were freely discussed. The dental societies studied various programs of children's dentistry and their relative costs.

The examination programs brought out the need for more adequate diagnostic equipment and facilities. Uniform office records were adopted by both physicians and dentists to provide for continuous supervision of children, and monthly summaries were integrated into health department records to keep up to date the information on the community health status.

Changing economic factors

The dentists who had seen altogether only a few hundred children in the course of a year, now examined and worked on thousands in their offices. Their practices took on new characteristics. They found, for example, that in order to make adequate diagnoses they needed x-ray machines in their offices. They found that the average length of time required to provide regular dental care for a child was much shorter than for irregular repair of neglected children. The bill was correspondingly smaller. As a result a larger and larger proportion of people could afford to pay the smaller fee. The earlier the child went to the dentist, the shorter the time, the smaller the fee, and the more people could afford the service. The total income of the dentists increased, but instead of large payments from a few they received small payments from many. The effect on the economics of the problem was obvious.

Everyone benefitted

During the first years, all of the school children in the area received medical examinations, later the preschool children and infants were examined. Thousands of families received the benefit of continuing medical supervision and learned the value of it. The physicians gained an appreciation of the wide distribution of physical defects, of the need for a program to obtain an optimum health status for all the children, including protection against all preventable diseases. They had experience with educational techniques. They discovered the need for cooperation, what could be accomplished by it, and the satisfaction that comes from it. Medical societies cooperated with the schools, with the health department and with the parents in a group movement which required careful organization for its accomplishment. Furthermore, the physicians examined a large number of well children from their own districts that they would otherwise not have seen. These contacts increased their practices. This participation had many benefits other than those derived by the child.

NEW NEEDS

On the other hand, the physicians and dentists developed new needs. They found that they now required additional pieces of expensive equipment. Because of the cost, few physicians could afford all of this equipment in their own offices.

Diagnostic laboratories

Cooperative plans were adopted whereby community laboratory and x-ray service could be provided—sometimes in the local hospital and sometimes elsewhere if a hospital were not available. Equipment was provided by the Foundation when the local medical society requested the service and agreed that fees were to be figured on a cost basis, and where proper supervisory consultants could be obtained. The Foundation further agreed on this basis to make up any deficit during the experimental period. When modern diagnostic tests were made available on a cost basis, a really large proportion of the population could then afford the service. Once more the economic picture was changed. The tremendous increase in the number of these individual low cost services made up in a very short time for the loss of income from former high prices for a few such services. All but one of these laboratories were self-supporting at the end of twenty-four months,—half of them before the end of the first year.

These modern diagnostic facilities enabled the physicians to practice a quality of medicine equal to that of their confreres in the larger cities. As a result, many of their patients who had formerly gone to larger centers were content to remain at home for their medical care. This brought in turn a greater interest in more adequate hospital facilities.

Hospitals improved

Stimulated by their medical staffs the local hospital trustees requested the Foundation for scholarships to study modern hospital management. They inquired into the methods by which they could best discharge their own responsibilities, and how their hospitals might contribute to a more adequate solution of the larger social problems. On their return, they examined their own facilities from a new point of view and discovered ways and means for improving the local hospital service. They worked out plans for better quarters and facilities and proposed a construction program to be worked out in conjunction with the PWA. As a result the Foundation made grants in aid for the construction of a number of hospitals throughout the area which ultimately provided hospital facilities comparable to those in urban centers.

These facilities again stimulated the medical groups to better organization of the hospital medical staffs. Clinical and pathological conferences were inaugurated. Records were improved. Case histories were studied. Arrangements were made for the regular visits of special consultants. The general quality of service was improved again and again.

Maternity nursing service

Study by a joint committee of the combined medical societies of the facts about maternal and infant mortality from the records provided by the health departments led to the establishment of a maternity nursing service first in one county—later in all. In order to meet local needs, this was provided both inside and outside the hospitals. Nurses received special training in Chicago, Detroit and other maternity nursing centers. Hospital nursing supervisors took training courses. Special consultants were employed to assure the quality of the service. The public health nursing educational service of the county health departments was closely coordinated with the program. Finally, most physicians refused to accept maternity cases unless they were to be cared for by the delivery nursing service either in the home or the hospital.

Extension of service

The interest of the hospital trustees in both intra and extra-mural hospital service resulted in an increased interest in hospital pre-payment plans of various sorts and studies are now under way in some of the counties to find better methods for meeting and distributing these costs. The women's auxiliaries of the hospitals found the home delivery service so useful that they are now inquiring into ways and means of providing general home-nursing service by both graduate nurses and nursing aides.

SCHOOLS AWAKE

Health programs for mothers, infants, and preschool children were only parts of the picture. The school program required cooperative planning and action by the school administrators and teachers as well as the medical and dental professions and the health department. A strong reinforcing program of health education had to be developed.

Specific plans for professional postgraduate education had been worked out first with the physicians. They were accustomed to this idea and had made an approach to the problem. The dentists requested a similar program the second year, and courses were arranged at Chicago, Boston and New York.

Superintendents study problem

It was not surprising, then, that in the third year, school superintendents and principals brought forward a request for summer courses where "problems of school administration affecting the health of the child" could be studied as a unit. This conformed to the principle of "leaders first." One hundred superintendents and principals took these courses at Northwestern University and the University of Michigan.

During their study, the superintendents discovered that there were many other phases of the school program which affected the health of the child besides health education—the physical plant, the curriculum, the organization of work, rest periods, home study, the dining room—to name only a few. This realization brought about a general reconsideration of school affairs as a whole. Various professional associations of school administrators and teachers were organized to study these problems and to work out plans for their correction.

Board members go to school

School superintendents appreciated, perhaps better than anyone else, the various factors that pull first one way and then another in a community. For instance, superintendents are charged with the technical administration of the school system but they are supposed to carry out policies adopted by their boards of education. Many years of preparation are required for the training of a good superintendent. No time at all is required to prepare a citizen for duty on a school board that will determine the policies the superintendent is to carry out.

The policy forming board is characteristic of American organizations both governmental and private. These boards have important parts to play but ways and means are needed by which board members of all civic organizations—health departments, schools, libraries, hospitals, village councils, boards of supervisors, and many others—may learn what their responsibilities are, and what may be accomplished through the proper performance of their duties. The superintendents thought that perhaps it would not be amiss for some of our educational institutions to give some consideration to this problem.

Thus a new chapter in adult education was inaugurated. Special short courses for school board members were arranged at leading universities and other educational institutions. This proved to be a most important step in the development of community programs. Later these courses were broadened to include members of boards of supervisors, boards of health and other policy forming groups.

Parents study too

School superintendents also pointed out that, if they were to make the important changes in their school systems indicated by their studies, they would need not only the passive permission of the parents but their active cooperation. Consequently they asked for short courses for mothers and fathers. These were arranged, and parents became interested contributors to community activities.

Teacher training

Once a nucleus of community support had been developed for a reorganized program permitting the schools to become useful centers for community service and leadership, the superintendents could then follow through with plans for the continuing education of their teaching staffs,—not to prepare them for advanced degrees alone, but to make them better teachers. Nearly 2,000 school teachers took special courses on Foundation scholarships. Many teacher training institutions were called upon to provide unusual and worthwhile experiences for these teachers, both on the college campus and in their home communities, through workshops, field consultants, and extension courses. The quality of teaching was immeasurably improved.

Old problems seen in new light

Many of the school problems were related to the physical condition of the buildings. After the various groups concerned had gained personal knowledge of the potentialities offered by modern educational methods and had seen modern school programs in operation in other places they made detailed studies of the needs of their own communities involving both rural and village schools.

Legal complications

The problem in Michigan was (and still is) complicated by two state laws. The local real and personal tax for current operating purposes was limited to 15 mills. Schools could issue bonds for building improvements in excess of their share of this limit, but these bonds had to be retired within five years. For all practical purposes, this put an end to school construction. School districts could not take advantage of the PWA assistance under which schools were being built elsewhere throughout the country. There was no way that they could even bond for 55% of the cost of construction and hope to pay it off within a five-year period.

Communities study their schools

Citizens and school boards held meetings to review their needs. Many factors were considered. Was it most economical to modernize, transport, or consolidate? The history for the preceding ten years of the tax rate, the school enrollment, the preschool census, the school's financial situation, the salary paid the teacher, her qualifications, her postgraduate work, and the educational programs were all studied.

Rural schools

Rural school boards met together to work out joint problems. Boards of supervisors studied the school situation and its relation to the total tax burden. The county school commissioners provided effective leadership. Consultants from the state department of public instruction advised local representatives. County-wide committees studied furniture, pressure water systems, various types of heating plants. Contractors, carpenters, and plumbers worked on standard specifications. School boards obtained bids for the modernization work.

The real problem

Committees then approached the Foundation with estimates of the relative amounts to be paid by the school districts and by the Foundation. They based these proportions on what the school district could afford to accept from the Foundation and not on what the Foundation could afford to give the school district. This was important because it grew out of the realization that the real problem was not that the school door was hung on with bailing wire but that often many of the people in the school district did not care how it was hung. The committees recognized that the Foundation had money to invest and a sympathetic understanding of their problems, but that the Foundation could not buy the interest of the local school authorities nor of the parents who sent their children to such schools.

This problem of proper schools for rural children is one of the most important challenges to democracy today. Education is accepted as one of the major responsibilities of government. Democracy is supposed to work best in small units where the problems are well understood and where the representatives are personally known to the voters. The school districts are small, there can be no doubt as to the importance of their function. It is unfortunate that we cannot point with more pride to their accomplishments. It is as important to help achieve the possibilities offered by the democratic system as it is to defend it from attack.

Several hundred rural schools have been improved as a result of the joint effort of the communities and the Foundation.

Method of paramount importance

The process involved in modernizing these schools, which in effect, revitalized the sense of responsibility and opportunities of rural citizenship, was even more important than the physical improvements achieved. Foundation grants helped the districts to provide, among other things, pressure water systems, flush toilets, modern heating, good lighting, and adjustable and movable furniture; but reconstruction was always accompanied by community educational programs designed to bring the attitude of the community up to date and make the old expression "what was good enough for granddad is good enough for me" take on a new significance. Many citizens learned with all the thrill of a new discovery that the proper interpretation of this old adage was that our grandfathers felt that only the best that they could get was good enough for their sons.

Consolidation

These community studies of the rural school situation brought out the desirability of consolidation for many districts. The state department of public instruction gave invaluable aid to the local school boards in this work. The legal and financial obstacles to consolidation have already been reviewed. However, with Foundation assistance, twelve consolidated schools were built in the area, several of them under the PWA program. The cost of the operation and financing of these schools was kept below the total cost of the smaller schools they replaced.

Each consolidated school provided better qualified teachers, practical courses in agriculture, farm management and home economics, a farm workshop, a library, a combination gymnasium and auditorium, a dining room and kitchen, and facilities for such extra-curricular activities as the school band, glee club, dramatic club and the school paper. The "socializing" influence of the school was increased by its use as a community center for educational and recreational activities. The need for a broad and thorough educational program in the rural areas brought about by the regular migration of a large proportion of rural students to the cities was not overlooked, and the general studies were strengthened also.

Village schools

A direct result of the rehabilitation of rural schools was a modified program for the modernization of the village schools. Many of these also dated back to the eighties and nineties. In many instances the original furniture was still in use. Much needed space was often wasted in large seldom-used rooms. Unfortunately the books, teaching materials and methods were too often similarly antiquated. Space was adjusted to use. New, movable furniture replaced the old. New teachers' desks, filing cabinets and library tables were added. New dining room and kitchen equipment was installed. The modernized equipment permitted reorganization of curricula as well. The school personnel made the most of this opportunity by developing extensive educational activity programs for the parents and the taxpayers as well as the children.

Special education

The medical and dental examination programs and the corresponding educational programs in the schools brought out the need for various types of special education; sight-saving classes, orthopedic care, blind, deaf, speech correction, and so forth. Special programs were developed by the communities to meet these needs, sometimes with Foundation help for special equipment or the partial subsidy of a special school, sometimes without.

The Ann J. Kellogg School of the Battle Creek public school system is an example of a new philosophy in dealing with the normal as well as the under-privileged child. This school provides care for approximately three hundred handicapped children in its total enrollment of nine hundred. The crippled, blind, near blind, deaf, hard of hearing, mentally retarded, socially maladjusted, children with weakened hearts, and others needing special treatment are cared for. They receive treatment and education suited to their needs, but they are not stigmatized by segregation. They are fitted as rapidly as possible into regular classes of normal children so that they may early adjust themselves to the demands of a natural environment and to the competition of normal children.

Nutrition

The hiatus between the knowledge and practice of nutrition is nowhere greater than in our schools. In rural America particularly, little attention is paid to the meals that children must have during the school day. At the request of school authorities the Foundation has cooperated in many nutritional programs for both rural and village schools. Money has been granted for supplementary foods, for milk, and for equipment. Recently the programs of the federal government, including the Surplus Marketing Administration, and the activities of the Michigan State Agricultural College have greatly strengthened local interest and resources.

Here again, programs are considered more important than facilities, and the extent of Foundation participation has depended upon how clearly the schools have seen the opportunity for well integrated educational projects. As a rule these include not only health education and the various nutritional aspects of food—vitamins, calories, etc.—but domestic science, food preparation, food purchasing, garden plots, and dairying as well. Vocational training has been improved through experience in proper service, food handling methods, and the management of restaurants. Music and art departments have built projects around the dining room. Teachers have made the most of their opportunities to teach nutrition, cooperation, and table manners by having the children select, prepare, serve and eat the food. Prepared meals served in schools have done much to overcome the limited eating habits of many children.

The public health nurses have carried instruction into the homes, with much practical advice on relative food values and on how to get the most out of the food budget.

OTHER FACTORS

The dining room and hot lunch projects, of course, brought up the question of the safety of the milk and food supplies. This was another problem that required community action and tested the health departments' capacity for leadership—particularly the public health engineers.

Safe milk requires community cooperation

The milk program alone involved the cooperative activity of hundreds of people. Veterinarians took special courses at cooperating colleges. Milk plant operators went away for short courses in laboratory work. Meetings were held with milk producers. Visits were made to dairy farms. Cooperative community educational programs were worked out by the milk producers, the plant operators, and the health department. Professional societies adopted resolutions approving pasteurized milk. School boards studied their responsibilities for providing safe food supplies. Milk and food supplies were greatly improved—by the educational method.

The public health engineers found an educational problem confronting them, not only with food and food handlers but also on questions of proper water supply and sewage disposal. All improvements to school buildings had to be approved by the health departments. The school modernization program added emphasis to cooperative activities with school boards, with well-drillers, plumbers, and tradesmen of various kinds. Educational programs were developed for many of these groups similar to those that have already been discussed.

Farm boys and girls

Many farm boys and girls were unable to continue their education after finishing rural agricultural high school in spite of the importance of modern scientific methods in present-day farming. They could not be spared from their parents' farmsteads, or they could not afford the additional expense of agricultural college.

It was suggested by some of the forward looking educators that an intensive eight-week short course at the Michigan State College, held during months of the year when work on the farm was necessarily slack, could provide such out-of-school farm youths with some of the fundamentals they needed. Foundation scholarships overcame financial problems. Several hundred boys and girls have already taken such courses.

On their return home these young people have made many important improvements on farms, in dairies, and other places affecting the health and general welfare of their communities.

Youth organizations

Interest in the extra-curricular activities of school children brought about community studies of the various youth organizations and recreational programs. Experiences of children and adults alike at the camps also stimulated a desire for improvement of the generally inadequate local recreational programs.

Again the communities asked for, and the Foundation provided, scholarships for training courses for recreational and youth organization leaders. Practical instruction in recreational activities was included in the short courses and postgraduate work for teachers and out-of-school farm youths at their request. Committees were appointed to study community resources and to prepare recommendations for year-round recreational programs for all the people. When the leadership was strengthened and interest aroused, support for recreational facilities was not hard to find.

Sometimes Foundation help took other forms. Loan funds were provided 4-H Clubs so that children could borrow money to buy farm stock and learn the business of farming. Grants in aid were made for playgrounds, swimming pools, and similar facilities. The Youth Building in Battle Creek, with its gymnasium, pools, and workrooms is maintained as a recreational center by the City Civic Recreational Association with a Foundation subsidy.

Many groups study their relation to community

The problems of school children also overflowed into other fields. For example, the question of juvenile delinquency involved attitudes of law enforcement officers, probate judges, ministers, and other influential community groups. So requests from these groups were granted for short courses to study the relationship of the individual group to community problems and how they could best meet their obligations.

CAMPS

The recognition of the need for camps came partly as an outgrowth of the communities' study of the school problem. Modernized rural and village schools and new consolidated agricultural schools supplied many of the educational needs of rural youth, but there were still whole areas of

everyday living that even schools equipped with the finest teaching and physical facilities could not begin to explore. Theoretical instruction could be given in hygiene, for instance, but there was little opportunity for practice within the four walls of the school building. However, there were other factors. Youth organizations and community groups needed facilities for camping activities. There were certain classes of pre-delinquent children, children from broken homes, and others with special needs for whom a camping program seemed to offer opportunities that could be provided in no other way.

Statewide program

The need was answered by the construction of three year-round camps by the Foundation, the gift of a fourth to a youth organization, and assistance of various kinds to other special camps. Each Foundation camp has a capacity of approximately one hundred and fifty children during the three summer months and fifty children for the other nine months of the year. On an average, sixteen hundred children are in camp during the year. They are accepted not only from the seven counties but also from all over the State of Michigan. Well qualified teachers are included in the year-round staffs. The camp schools are licensed by the State Social Welfare Commission as boarding schools, and the school curriculum is recognized by the Michigan State Department of Public Instruction.

Purpose

The primary purpose of the camp schools is not recreation but the training of youngsters in practical preparation for life and citizenship in a democracy. The children learn that responsibilities and privileges go hand in hand. To the study of the three R's are added the areas of experience needed to round out the education of the whole child: social living, healthful living, work-experience, and the profitable use of leisure. Classrooms are supplemented by out-of-door activities with ample opportunities for nature study, "trading posts" where the children conduct the camp stores, home economics rooms, and workshops. The whole process of working and living together with sympathetic friends for instructors is a valuable experience for teachers and parents as well as for children. The important contributions of this type of community camp school are being increasingly recognized as a result of this experimental work.

Camps as community resources

These camps strengthen the local community resources and cooperate closely with the schools. The uses to which they have been put have varied greatly. They have been used as reorientation centers for children from homes which social agencies are trying to reorganize before sending the children back to them, and where special care and education is needed in the interim. Children with orthopedic defects have been cared for. Children who had been in contact with individuals ill with tuberculosis have been built up to a more robust health. Pre-delinquent children have found a new sense of security and appreciation in these camps. Whole classes and entire rural schools have gone to camp for two-week periods with their teachers for experiences in living together. Training courses for waterfront leaders or leaders for youth or recreational organizations have been held. Occasionally the camps have been used for special adult institutes or county-wide meetings of teachers or for workshops for camping personnel. They have been used for "Mothers' Camps," where instruction and recreation have gone hand in hand. The camp schools have given care to thousands of children and have played an important part in the education of the communities they have served.

NEW BOOKS FOR OLD

All of these educational programs for the various professional and lay groups in the communities taxed the local library resources. The state and college libraries were unable, because of their distance from the area, to provide the books and reference materials necessary to keep these projects moving. Consequently the Foundation established a professional library in connection with its own offices in Battle Creek. This can be drawn upon by anyone in the seven counties by simply mailing a postcard to the librarian, the book requested being sent by return mail without charge.

Education of librarians and trustees

As a result of the increased interest in the use of library facilities and the new programs in the schools, a need for special courses for librarians was brought out. Courses were organized both for professional librarians and for library trustees. When they returned to their districts they made analyses of the local facilities both in schools and in the community libraries and reported appalling conditions. School and local libraries showed low circulations. Library trustees would not invest money in books because "they were not read anyhow."

Inventory is taken

A study of the books on the shelves by local committees, aided by library consultants, indicated that people showed good judgement in not reading the outworn, out-of-date volumes that filled the shelves. Most of them were in print so taxing to the eyes that no intelligent child or adult these days would inflict such a task on himself, even if the subject material were of interest.

Library practice was as bad as the books. Large school libraries were locked up at the end of the day and during the summer months. Village libraries were not available to rural residents.

At the request of a local group, the Foundation loaned 1800 volumes experimentally to a county library. Circulation of these books proved so astonishing that the local committee recommended an extension of the loan library service and an exchange program for all seven counties was developed.

Library days

In order to remove the old encumbrances to the reading habits of the rural people, the Foundation agreed to give one new book to the local school and village libraries for every five old ones that were turned in. The old books were to be sold for paper and the proceeds turned over to the local library council. It seemed appropriate that, while the old world burned new books, the new world should destroy old books. The counties organized ten-day collection drives, culminating in library days—and nearly a million old books were turned in.

Book fairs

Committees were then organized to study local library problems, to develop methods for the selection of the new books, to formulate plans for the cooperative exchange of both new and old books (good enough to be retained) between township and school libraries within convenient areas. Occasionally these were linked with a county library system. Book fairs held in the fall were attended by nearly fifty thousand people. Library consultants were engaged to discuss the books and help the children, teachers, and librarians select the new ones. The Foundation helped for one additional year by matching all new book purchases for a twelve-month period.

Cooperation pays

The Foundation was interested, not only in the provision of better educational and recreational material for the children, but also in the lessons in cooperation to be learned by the communities and their leaders. Four schools and a near-by village library, for example, each of which were to receive 200 books from the Foundation, learned that they could go their own separate ways and get only 200 titles apiece, or with a little planning they might exchange lists and books and make 1000 titles available to their respective clients. The money paid by the Foundation would be the same in either case, but cooperation would get them five times as many books as money would alone. Cooperation would, of course, pay the same dividends for the old books retained without any new expenditure of funds. Consequently it was important to exchange not only the titles of new books but also the lists of old books retained at the end of the campaign. The lesson was obvious.

Other implications

The experience gained by some of the school authorities in providing better library service to their communities opened their eyes to the possibility of using some of their other facilities for recreation and training for adults as well as for children. Thus many schools became real community centers, and auditoriums, gymnasiums, and shops were opened to adults. The extra cost necessary to operate a building for the additional hours in the evening did not seem too great when there was a real community demand from the citizens themselves.

LOCAL RESOURCES ARE SOMETIMES DISTANT

Facilities for professional education in the graduate and continuing-education levels were so limited it was necessary to go far afield to find enough colleges and institutions interested in this type of adult education to meet the demands of the program. This was not surprising. The responsibility of professional schools for graduates with problems is not well enough recognized to warrant any expectation that they would undertake projects unless there is an important problem to be solved in which local leaders are sufficiently interested to demand help. Professional people in turn are often unaware of their own needs until called upon to participate in active programs. Generalized adult education under formal auspices is not the answer. Leadership from above or outside the community is not enough. A local focus on a field problem is needed to achieve proper understanding and lasting results.

So it can be seen that the problem-solving approach led from one program to another with a constantly increasing effect upon the communities. Since community resources often include cultural or educational centers removed an appreciable distance geographically from the local scene the problems uncovered in the area sometimes led to programs undertaken elsewhere. For example, the educational work with dentists and in the field of public health led to grants in aid to the University of Michigan for the establishment of the first school of postgraduate dentistry in the world. Another grant matched by the Rockefeller Foundation made possible a new School of Public Health at the University of Michigan. Other grants were made:

To the University of Michigan to strengthen the Department of Pediatrics, to provide consultant service, and for research work on anemias of pregnancy and the newborn.

To the Michigan Department of Health for research work on diarrhea and enteritis of the newborn, and for consultants in obstetrics and nutrition.

To the University of Michigan and the Michigan Joint Committee on Health Education for the development of syndicated newspaper articles, public lectures, and radio talks.

To the Michigan Infantile Paralysis Commission and the Michigan Poliomyelitis Commission for statewide consultants for the diagnosis and treatment of children stricken with infantile paralysis.

To the Michigan Nurses Association for training out-of-service nurses to help alleviate the shortage of nurses brought on by the national emergency.

To the Health Department of the City of Detroit for the study of tuberculosis, measles, scarlet fever, and typhoid fever.

To Columbia University for ten-year research in rheumatic heart disease in children.

To the Health Section of the World Federation of Education Associations for the international exchange of health education material.

To the American Public Health Association for the Rural Health Conservation Contest in the United States and Canada, and for epidemiological studies on the control of communicable diseases.

To Harvard University for a field hospital and laboratory in England for the study of communicable diseases of children under war-time conditions.

The Foundation has contributed to Battle Creek social agencies and youth organizations. The W. K. Kellogg Junior High School and auditorium was presented to the city of Battle Creek.

Other grants of a similar nature have been made. These are itemized in the Treasurer's Report.

A MULTIVERSITY

It was natural that the Foundation's relationships with professional schools should result in requests from them to use this area for the training of some of their advanced students.

Professional students in all fields have never been better prepared than they are today as far as their scientific and academic work is concerned. Through this very concentration and the constantly increasing proportion of their lives spent within the halls of learning, theory has been increased at the cost of experience.

The need

When he gets his degree, the young physician knows a great deal about the streptococcus and about the biochemistry of the body. He knows something about that body as a patient. He knows very little about the family of that patient and rarely anything about the community in which that family lives. The teacher at graduation knows more than any other teacher before her about the subject she is to teach. She even knows a good deal about how to teach. She knows astonishingly little about the child she is going to teach. All of her troubles come, curiously enough, not from teaching subjects, but from teaching children. The public health engineering graduate knows exactly how to pasteurize milk and how to insure a good water supply. He knows practically nothing about how to get a community to install a safe water supply or to want pasteurized milk.

The professional student who is going to work with people and who is unable to supplement his technical knowledge acquired at school with actual experience with people and their problems is but half prepared to accept his responsibilities intelligently and effectively.

The opportunity

It was evident that there was a grave lack of organized areas where professional workers could learn about family life and community organization. The seven counties cooperating with the Foundation seemed to present an unusual answer to this need. The district is rural. The inter-relationships of the various community groups and individuals can easily be traced. The seven modern county health departments coordinate the full resources of the respective counties in active and varied programs. Record systems have been specially prepared to sum up the health and sanitation picture at a glance, not only for staff but also for student use. There are detailed maps and special studies of the problems and resources of the communities. Most important of all, the physicians, dentists, teachers, and other community leaders who are working with actual problems in life situations are well prepared to accept their responsibility in a cooperative training program. They see an opportunity to spread their philosophy and to repay the universities at the same time for interest taken in their local problems. The district has sufficient area, population, and variety of problem-solving activities to absorb a large number of students without inconvenience. It is small enough for effective supervision and easy exchange of experiences.

The Fellowship Program

Accordingly, the Foundation's Fellowship Program was inaugurated experimentally in 1934 with four students who came to the area as Fellows in public health engineering. Since then hundreds of young men and women have had field experience in the seven counties. Graduate and undergraduate students are now accepted in medicine, dentistry, nursing, engineering, teaching, hospital administration, public health administration, library work, camping, sociology, veterinary science, and government. The Foundation now provides this experience for selected students recommended by more than thirty universities. These students are able to make their early mistakes under supervision.

Fellowship students are recommended by the deans of the various professional schools. The stipends are modest but adequate to cover living expenses.

Types of training

The experience is offered at four levels: studentships, scholarships, fellowships, and assistantships. Studentships provide from a week to a month of observation in the area as a part of a university training course. Scholarships provide three months of observation and field experience, either for credit as part of a university course or to round out academic work. Fellowships provide graduate students nine months to a year of observation and field experience, including administrative responsibility under university supervision. Assistantships are one year appointments to the staffs of Foundation consultants and provide experience with analytical and administrative problems as well as service as consultants.

Throughout the student's experience the emphasis is upon participation and practice, and not upon theory or the acquisition of more technical knowledge. The reports of these students add bit by bit to the accumulating store of information about the area and its problems, and so they help the communities who have tried to help them in return for the aid they themselves have received.

SUMMARY

What is now known as the Michigan Community Health Project has been a joint effort on the part of the citizens of seven counties in southwestern Michigan and the W. K. Kellogg Foundation to improve the health, happiness, and well-being of rural children, both present and future, to improve the social and physical environment, and to assist in the development of well-organized community plans for health service, education, and social welfare.

The project is designed not only to give direct service to the local children but also as a laboratory and training center where answers may be sought to pressing professional and sociological questions facing the country today. Here fundamental problems involving health promotion, care of the sick, education, and recreation are being worked out on a local basis. Here young people studying to take their places in the various professions are coming face to face with field problems on a new and practical level.

The undertaking decided upon was not one of providing services to an impoverished area. The people within the Michigan Community Health Project are fairly well supplied with resources both human and physical. The challenge was to determine to what degree local leadership can be stimulated to achieve the potentials offered by the American, democratic, cooperative way of life in developing really effective methods to meet community needs and thus advance the cause of child health, education, welfare and recreation at local, state, and national levels.

The methods chosen have been intended not only to help the children now assisted but to improve the skills of the professional people and the facilities of the communities rather than to make them dependent upon an outside agency, so that future children also will be better cared for whenever the Foundation support is withdrawn.

The approach is new in the sense that this is the first time that an effort has been made on a community basis to work at more or less the same time on all of the major factors affecting the child.

The specific objectives for the communities included in the Project are the nineteen points set forth so clearly in the Children's Charter of the White House Conference on Child Health and Protection.

The plan that has been followed in moving toward these several objectives has involved:

First, the definition and measurement of community problems.

Second, the organization of individuals facing similar problems.

Third, the stimulation of these groups through the presentation to them of local problems about which they should be concerned.

Fourth, the development of specialized adult education programs to prepare these groups for better service, including the strengthening of educational and consultation centers at higher levels.

Fifth, financial assistance over a limited period in programs set up by local groups where the individuals may gain first-hand experience in problem solving.

Sixth, grants in aid for buildings and equipment necessary for proper functioning of programs when maintenance and operation costs can be met from local resources.

No demonstration has been attempted and consequently the continuance or discontinuance of many of the programs developed cannot be used to measure the success of the Foundation's contribution. Each dollar that has been spent has brought returns in direct service. There can be little doubt but that the communities are much nearer the goal set eleven years ago than they would have been without Foundation assistance. The programs in the schools, hospitals, libraries, health departments, and the professional services of medicine and dentistry speak for themselves.

During the next few years, the Michigan Community Health Project will move forward and its community leaders will attack new problems. Foundation aid for many of the projects carried on in the past will undoubtedly be discontinued. New projects will be started. It is hoped that the area will continue for many years to serve as a laboratory for the study of social problems and as a training center for young professional people.

A long road must still be travelled before really adequate answers to many rural community needs will be found. The people have complete responsibility for the continuance of the programs and for the justification of the expenditure of funds. The degree to which they will be able to realize the potentialities that their plans afford lies entirely with them.

The potentials of cooperative endeavor in the American communities to meet social needs have not yet been even scratched. The Michigan Community Health Project has shown some of the techniques that may lead to wider horizons.

The Foundation's contribution in the future will point toward a further extension of resources and facilities to meet these needs, not only in Michigan but in other parts of the United States as well.

THE
MICHIGAN COMMUNITY HEALTH PROJECT
A Pictorial Review

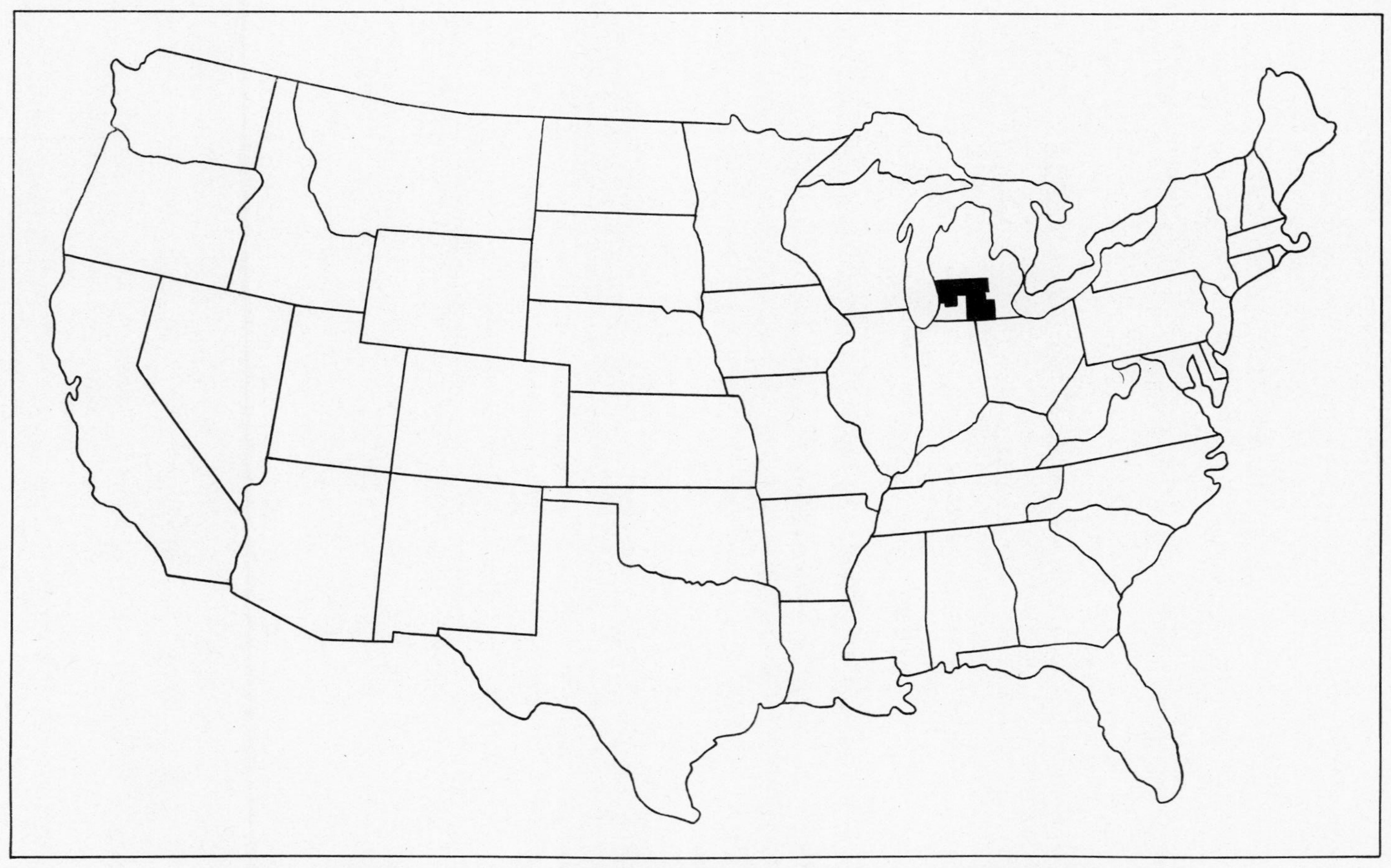

THE MICHIGAN COMMUNITY HEALTH PROJECT

"While food, raiment, and shelter are necessities, and while it is essential that the educational facilities be maintained on high levels, it is only through cooperative planning, intelligent study, and group action—activities on the part of the entire community—that lasting results can be achieved."

Program begins when local committees seek Foundation cooperation in solution of community health and education problems

Widespread interest and participation assured by signed requests from virtually all professional and lay organizations

Boards of supervisors of seven counties create official health departments in five successive years

Seven health departments are housed in buildings provided by counties

Three-man health committees of boards of supervisors meet regularly with county director to determine policies and expenditures

Public health nurses and engineers under direction of medical health officer find local problems and help solve them

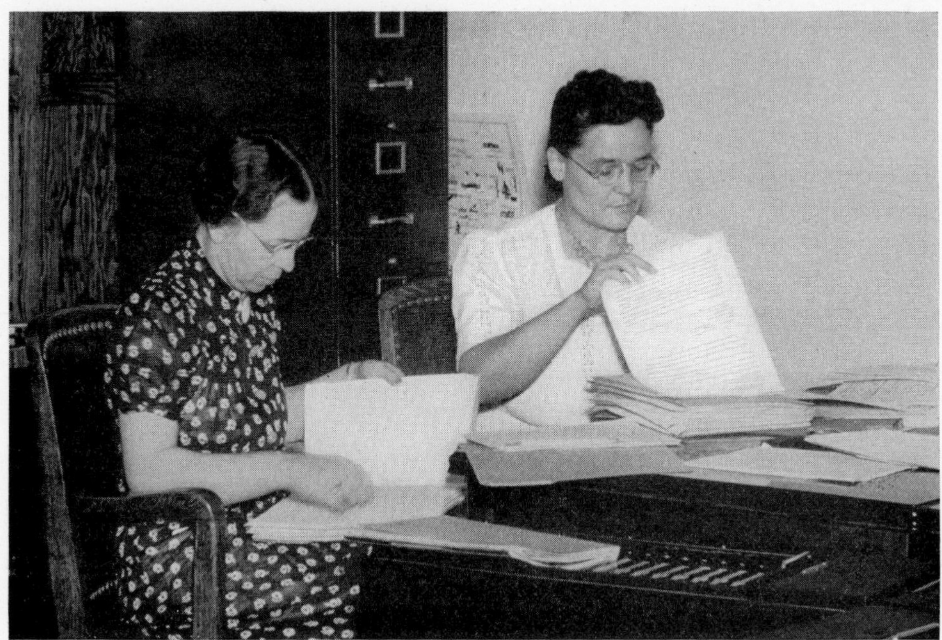

Modern business tools bring problems into focus and permit effective use of time and personnel

County medical and dental societies study health needs of county with health departments and work out cooperative programs

School programs are developed by county school commissioners, school committees of boards of supervisors, superintendents and teachers

Parent and community organizations study local needs and work out details of their participation in health and education programs

Seven county directors meet regularly with Foundation Field Director to discuss area problems, test plans, and share experience

Joint meetings of seven county field staffs permit rapid pooling of experience and consultation with Federal and State officials

Advice of state and national professional societies and voluntary agencies is sought regularly and programs are coordinated

Foundation consultants on medicine, dentistry, schools, hospitals, nursing, engineering, and libraries help local communities

Comparison with 300 United States and Canadian counties is afforded by Rural Health Conservation Contest subsidized by Foundation

County wide advisory committees with representatives of major groups coordinate programs of all community organizations

Medical societies request Foundation scholarships for postgraduate courses as preparation for intensive programs

Additional funds make it possible for county medical societies to hear outstanding experts in special fields

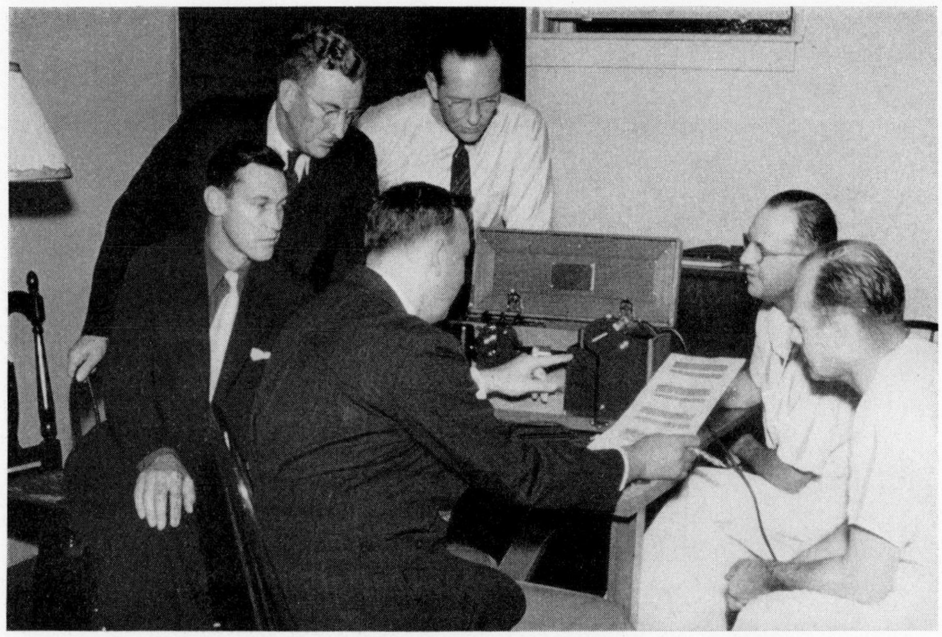

Special equipment coupled with visiting consultant service for physicians and hospitals permit review of difficult cases

University of Michigan and State Health Department subsidized consultants improve hospital staff conferences

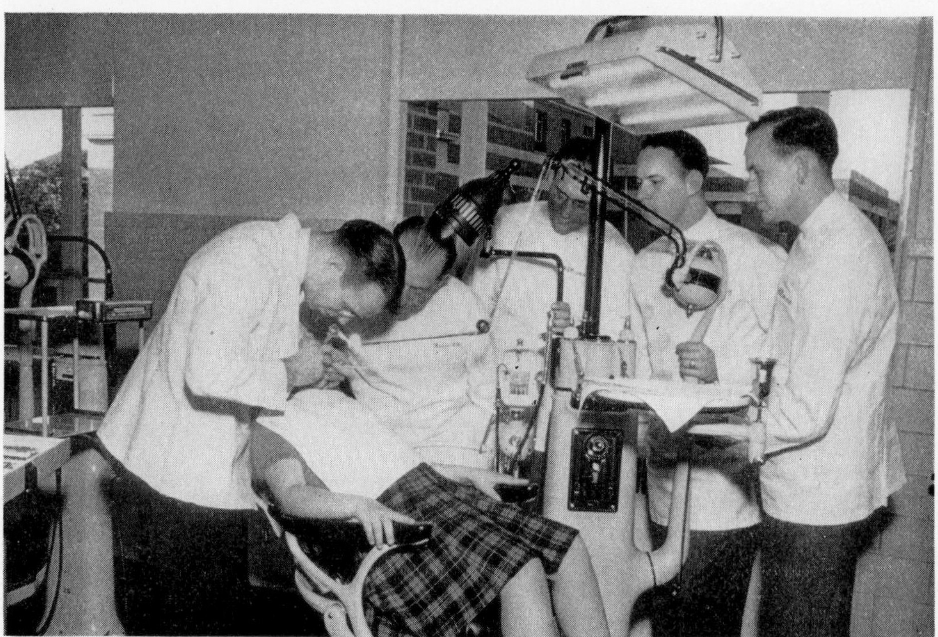

Dental societies request Foundation scholarships for postgraduate training in children's dentistry

First Institute for Postgraduate Dentistry was built by University of Michigan with Foundation and P.W.A. aid

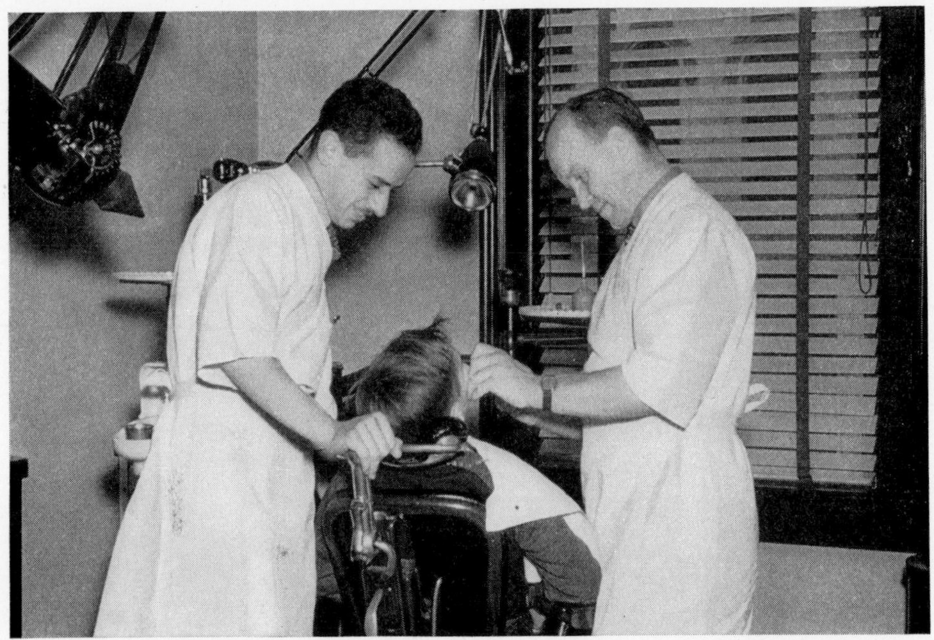

Dentists, too, are able to review problem cases in their own offices with visiting consultants

Dental Societies request Foundation scholarships for office assistants and special courses are developed

School superintendents and principals ask for scholarships to study problems of school administration affecting child health

School teachers receive scholarships for summer courses at universities or university-sponsored workshops in local communities

Extension courses are given by field consultants from Universities of Michigan, Chicago, and Northwestern, with Foundation funds

Consultants work with individual teachers in rural and graded schools

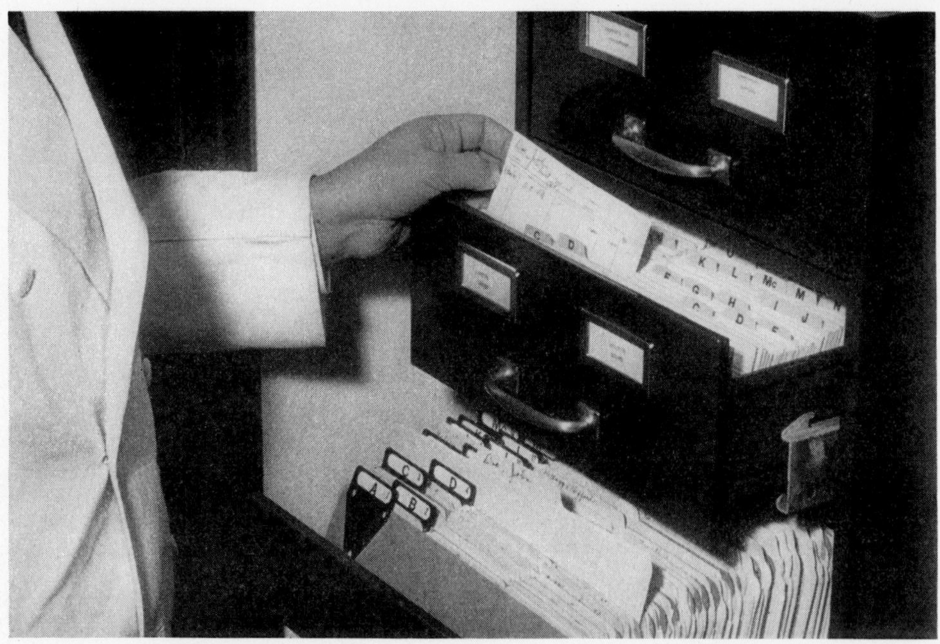

Uniform office records adopted by physicians and dentists make continuous supervision of children possible

Special card file with tickler system assures regular follow-up of children by physicians and dentists

Schools receive information necessary to adapt instruction to children's health needs and to reinforce health programs

Summaries of medical and dental services integrated into official records monthly keep case records and basic information up to date

Mothers report for prenatal medical supervision early in pregnancy

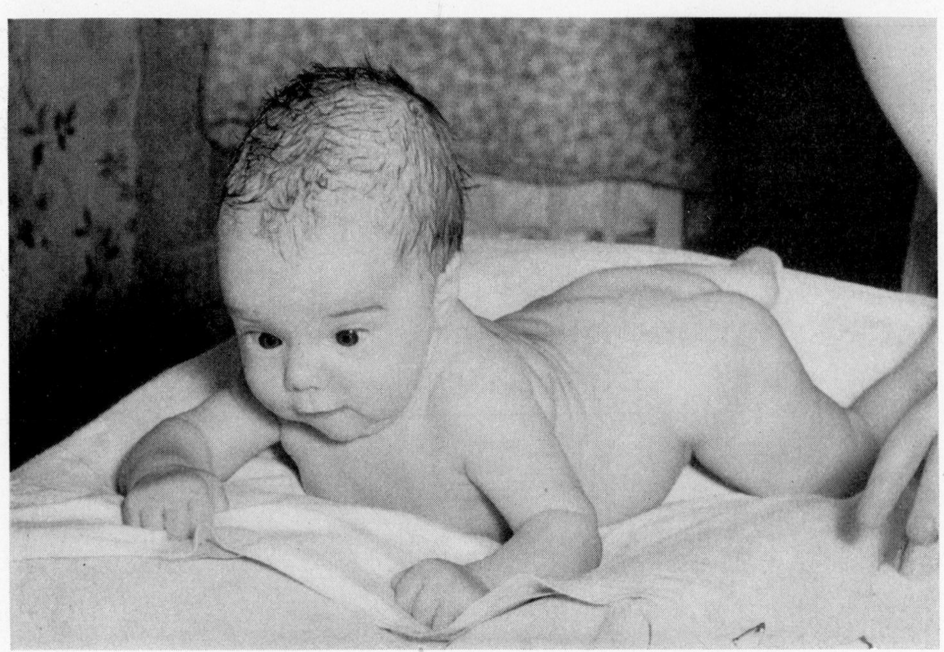

Infants receive regular medical supervision

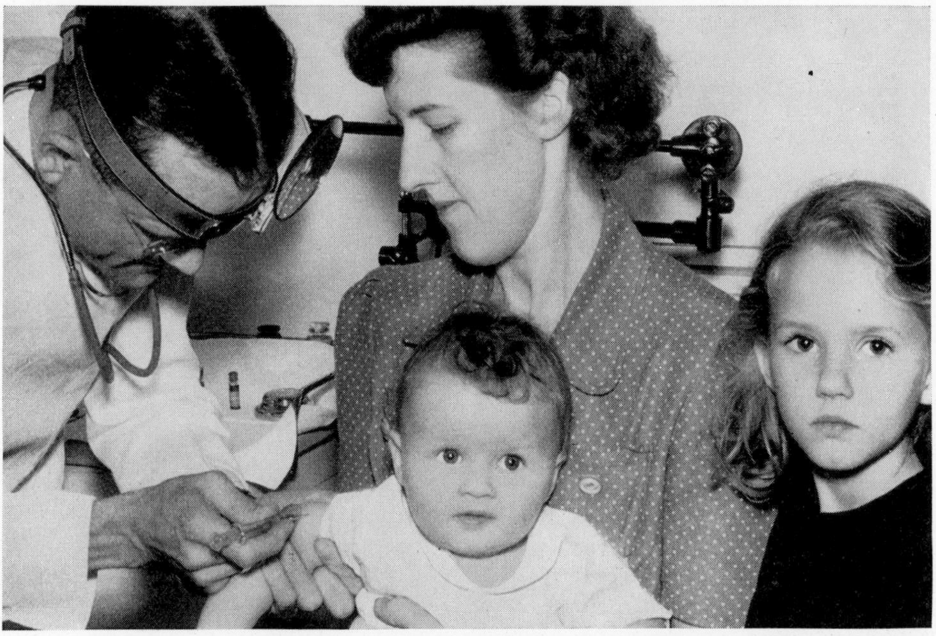

Children are immunized against diphtheria near the first birthday. All work is done in offices of private physicians

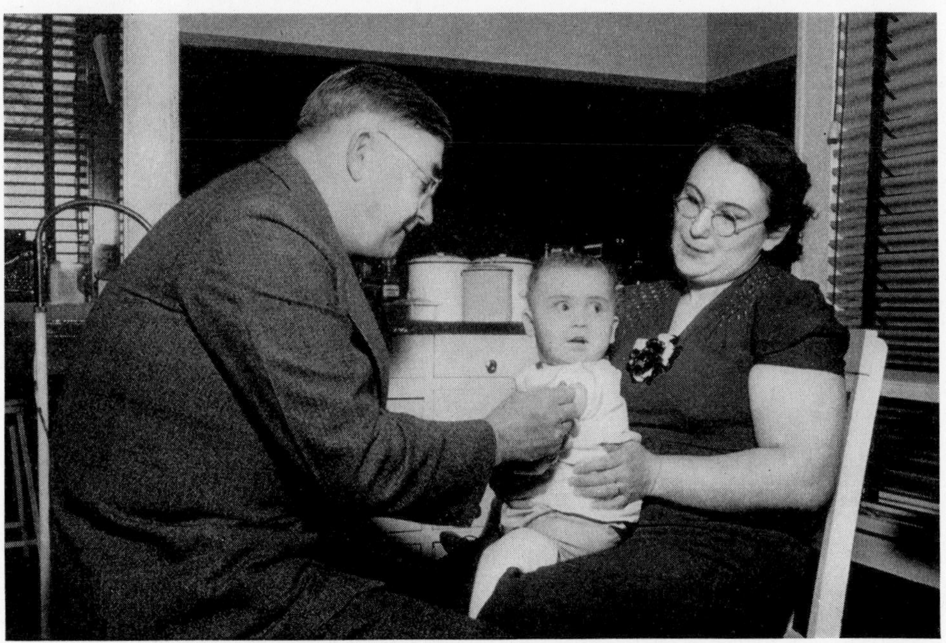

They are also vaccinated against smallpox. Health department contributes toward cost if physicians approve parents' request for aid

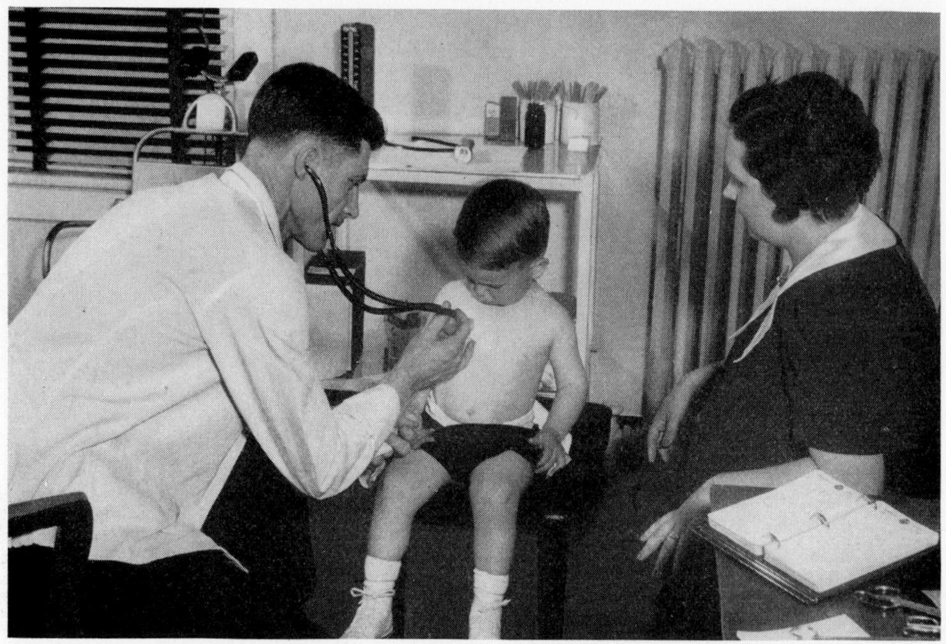

Pre-school children receive medical supervision

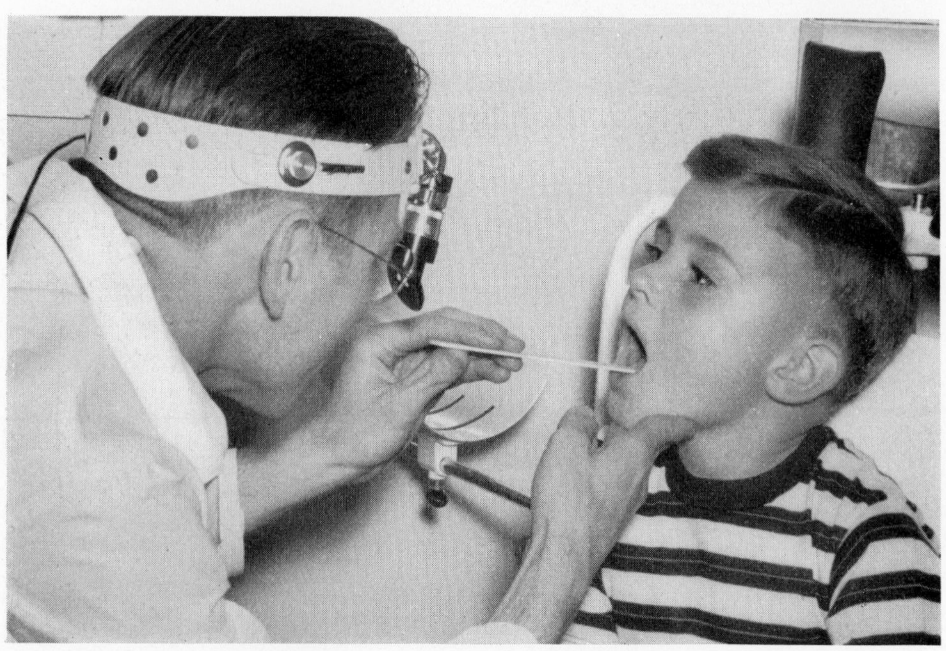

Program for school children is continuation of supervision already established

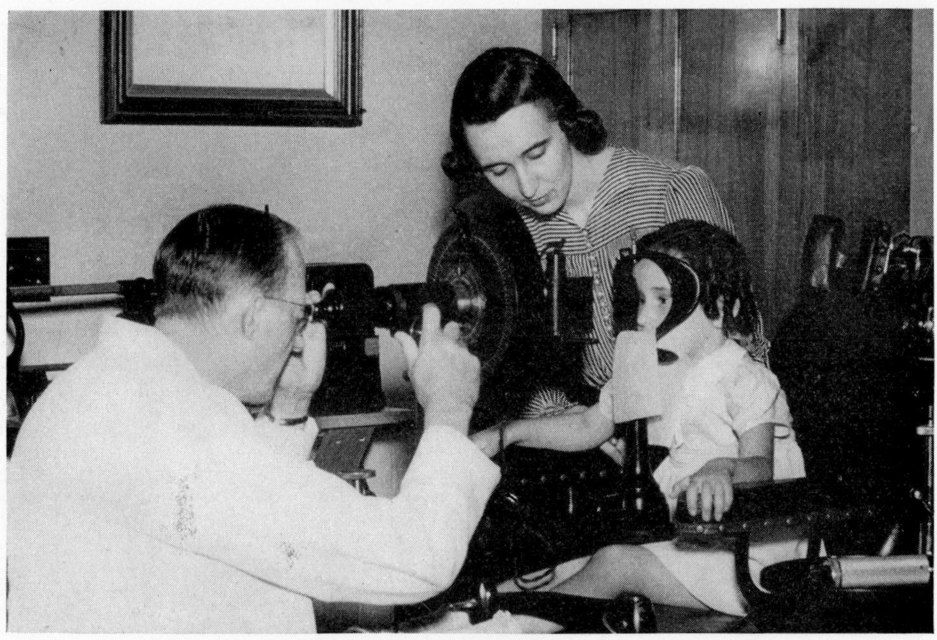

Defects are corrected as found. Health department contributes for needy cases when physicians approve parents' request for aid

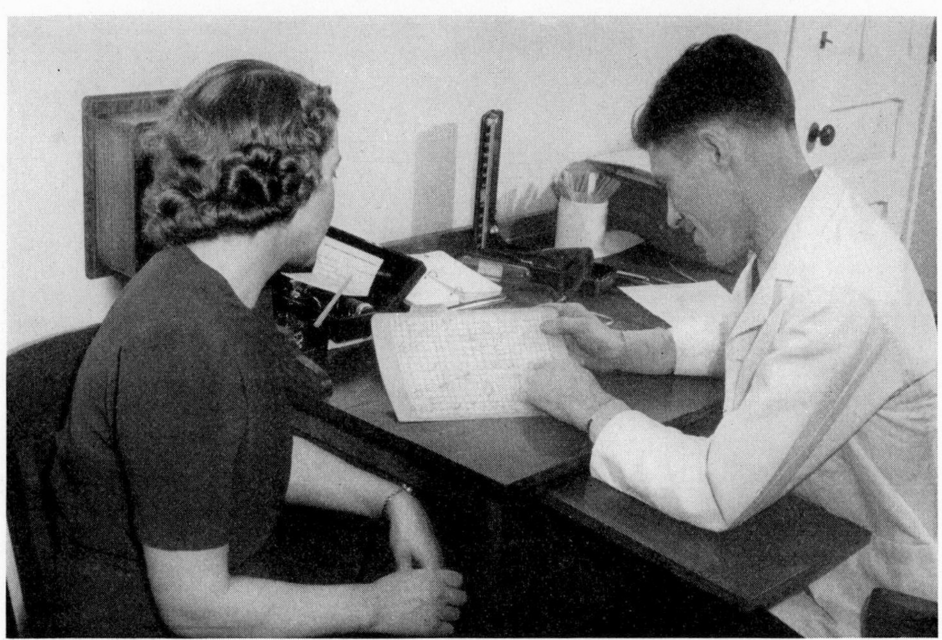

Public health nurses contact physicians and dentists regularly, assist in follow-up, provide constant liaison

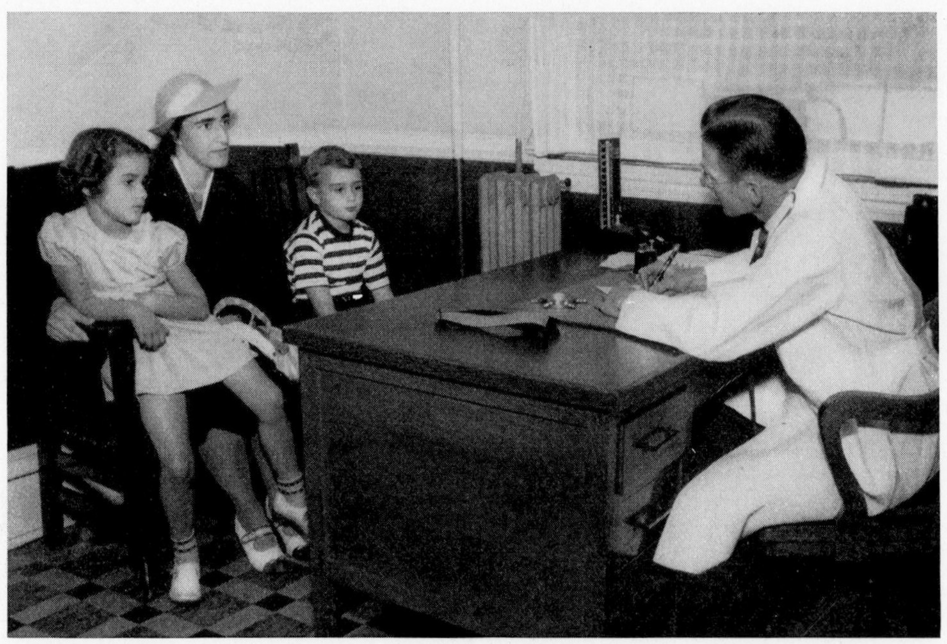

Physicians recommend starting of dental care before children are three years of age

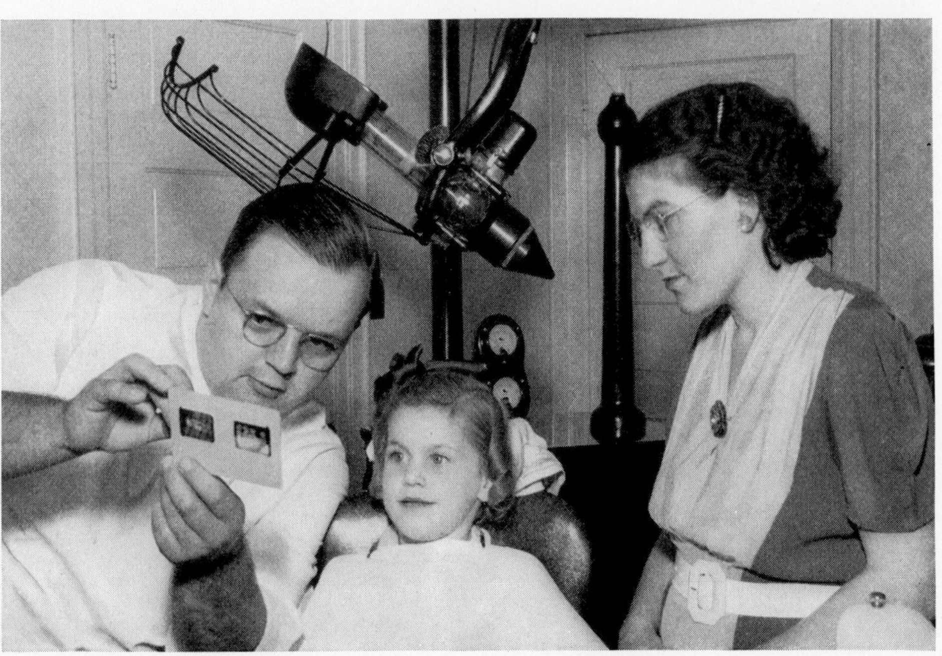

Dentists adopt uniform methods including x-ray for examinations and visual education of children and parents. There are no clinics

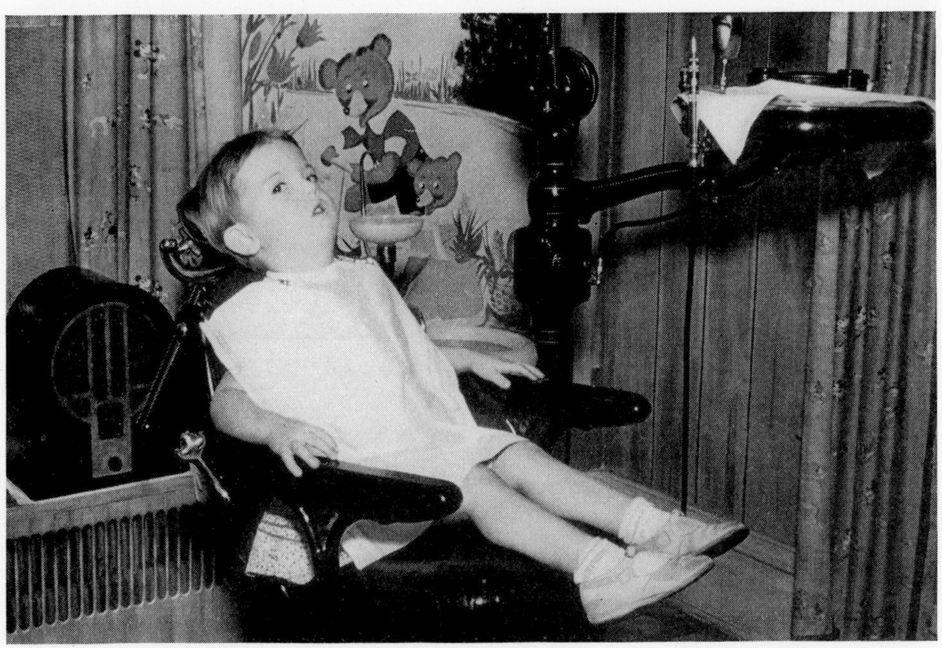

Children start continuous dental care during preschool years. Early and regular visits keep cost low so more can afford care

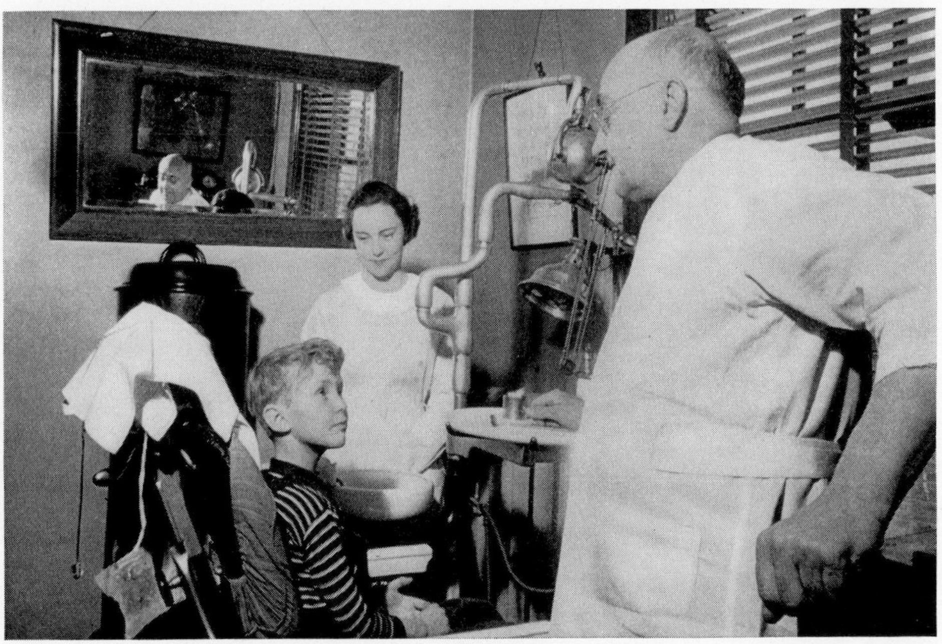

Dental program carries children forward. Health department contributes toward cost if dentists approve parents' request for aid

Public health nurses give advice in the homes and assist in getting children under medical and dental supervision

Public health nurses demonstrate advantages of proper care to many parent groups during course of year

Physicians and dentists meet with teachers to plan reinforcing school program and coordinate activities

Physicians and dentists take part in instruction of school children and parents

Children question physicians and dentists before starting classroom project. The professional man is the children's friend

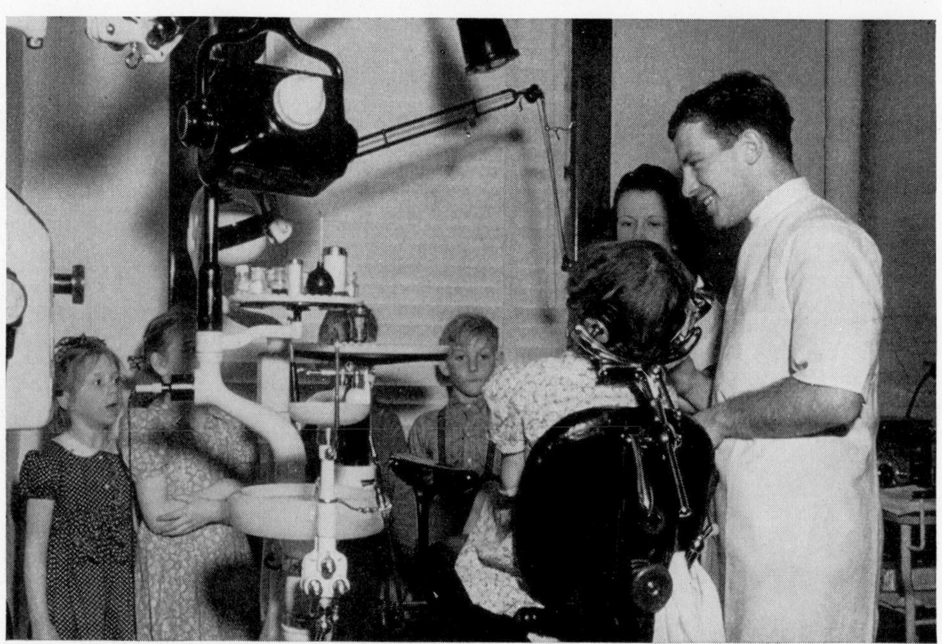

Offices are visited and equipment explained at a time when no work is to be done. Familiarity prevents fear

Health habits and attitudes are created by classroom projects developed by the children

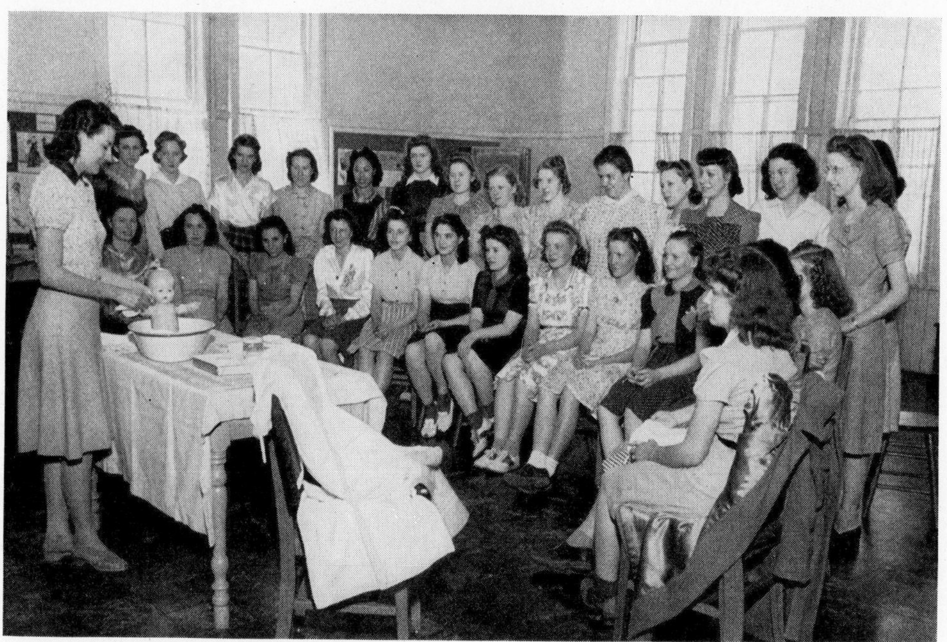

Project method extends throughout school program to include demonstrations of home hygiene and baby care by older girls

Problem cases are reviewed at conferences of psychologists, teachers, physicians, public health nurses, and social workers

Facilities for all types of special measurements are available at Western Michigan College of Education through Foundation aid

Remedial reading classes are conducted by local teachers trained through Foundation scholarships

Special facilities and trained teachers have been made available for speech correction

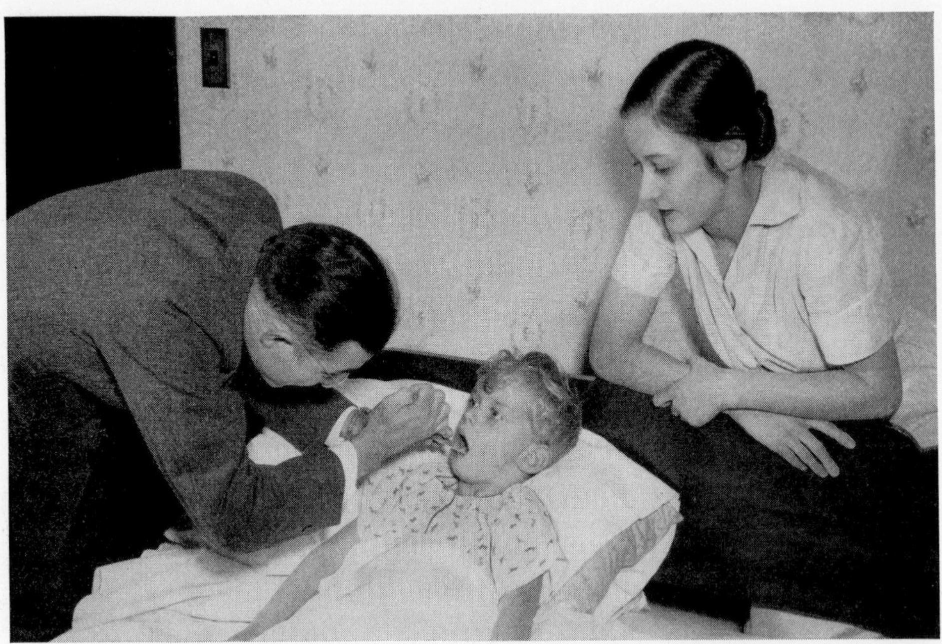

Physicians take postgraduate training in communicable diseases. Health departments pay for diagnostic call if parents cannot

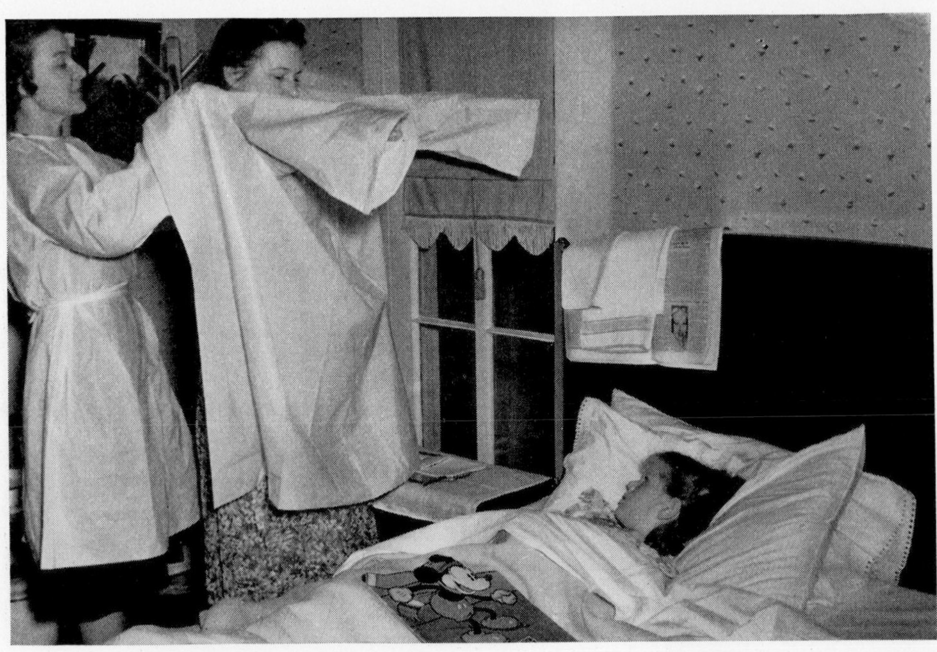

Public health nurses instruct family on care of sick and how to protect other members of family and community

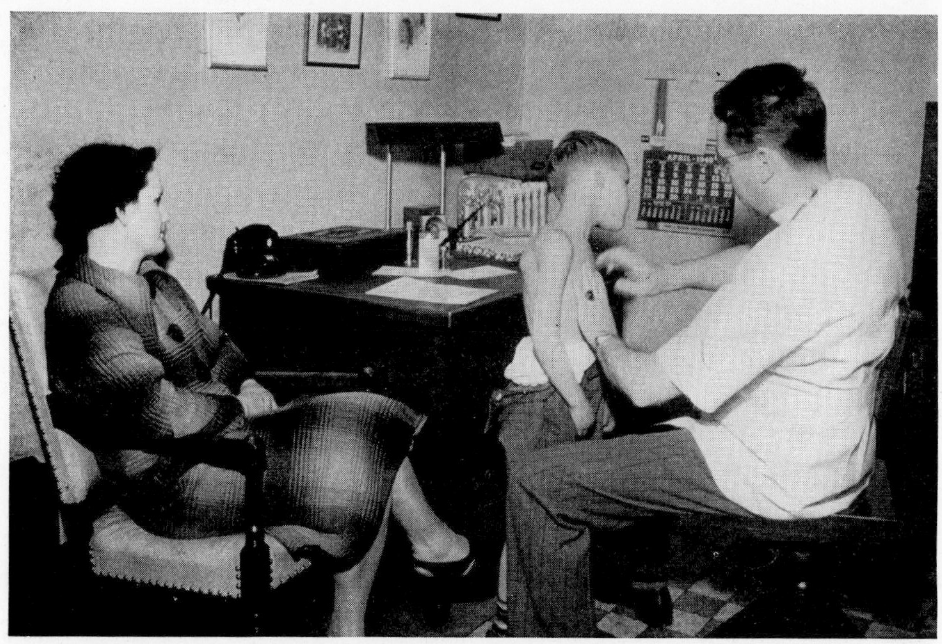

Tuberculosis cases are hospitalized. Contacts are followed up and examined by family physicians with health department assistance

Public health nurses consult regularly with teachers and school directors on health problems and education programs

Probate judges study child dependency and delinquency in Chicago and Detroit, and work closely with health departments

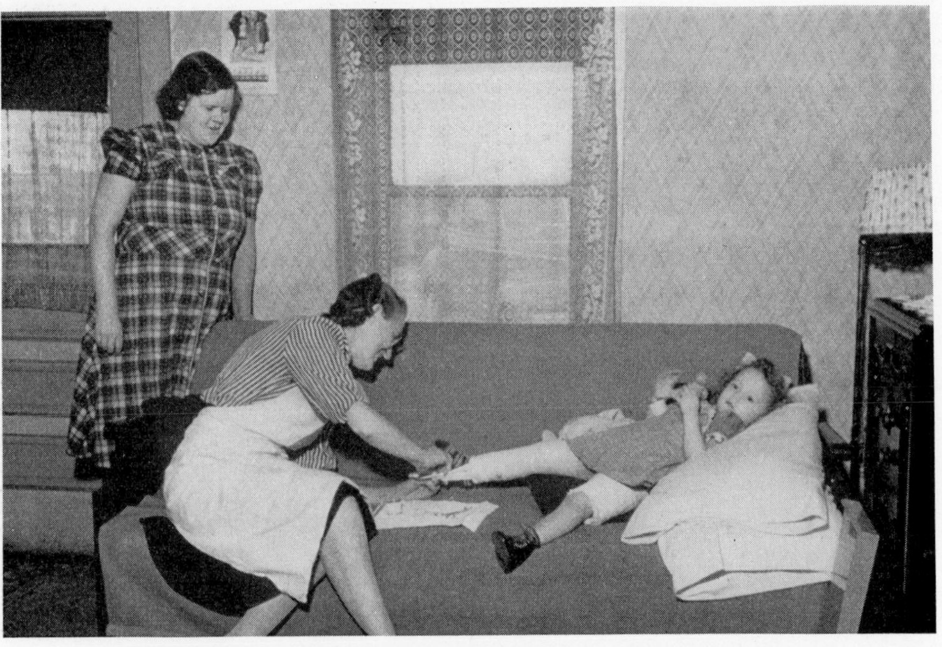

Public health nurses with special orthopedic training follow cases and give limited home care under direction of orthopedic surgeons

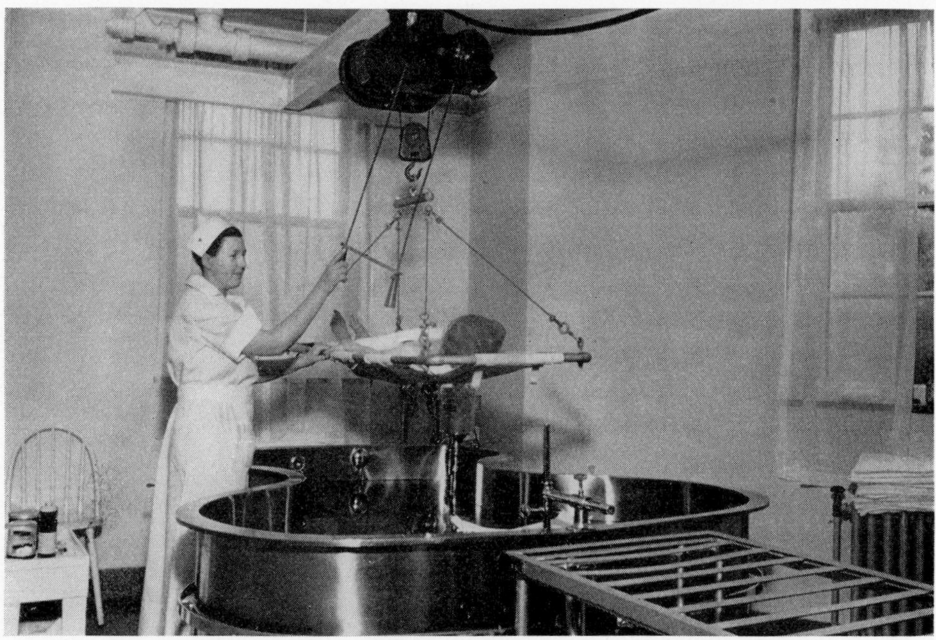

Special hydrotherapy and other equipment provided hospitals permit local care of difficult cases

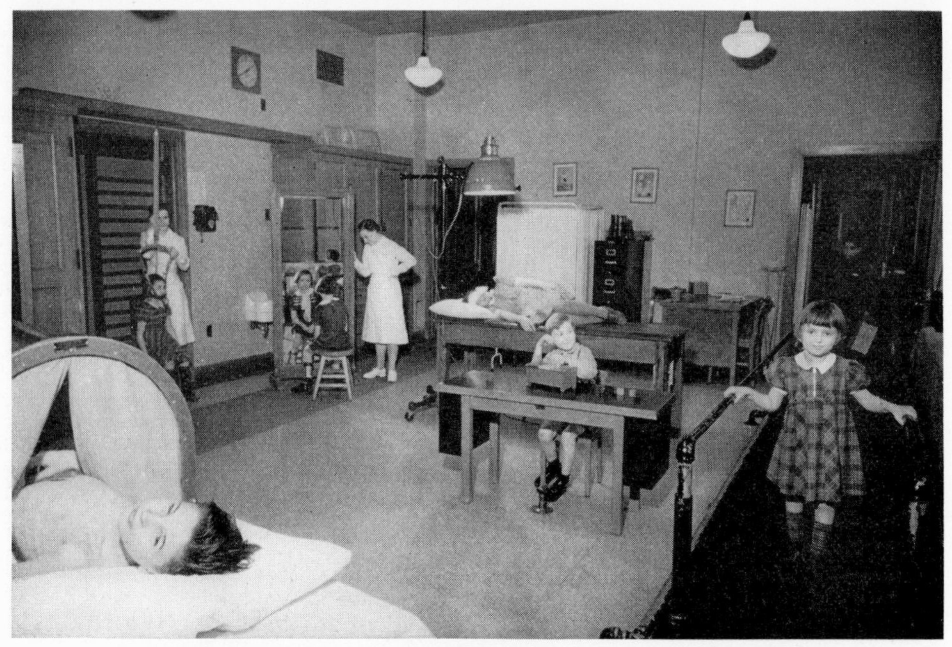

Exceptional facilities at Ann J. Kellogg School in Battle Creek make it possible to fit children into classes of normal youngsters

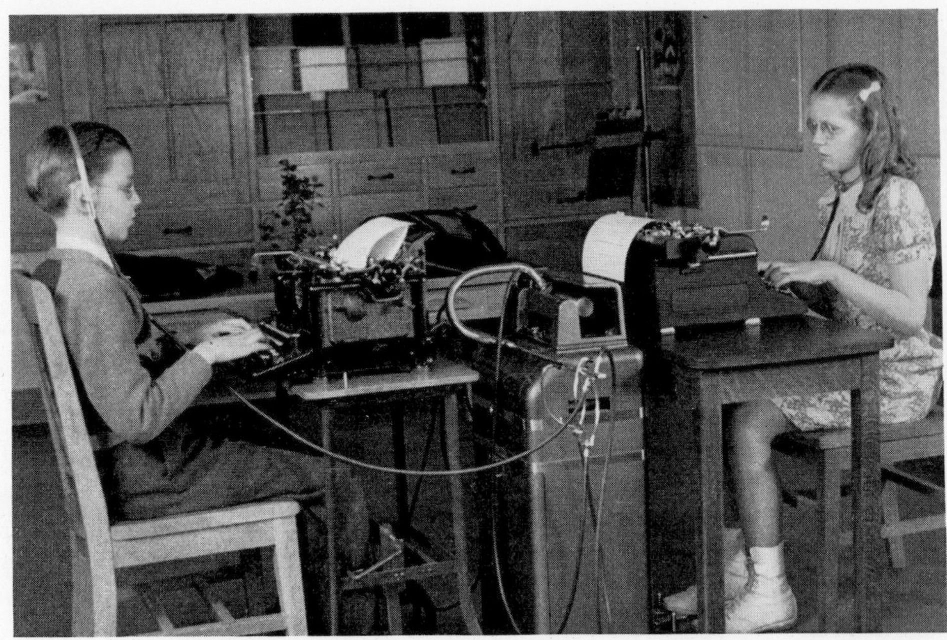

Sight saving classes in public schools conserve vision

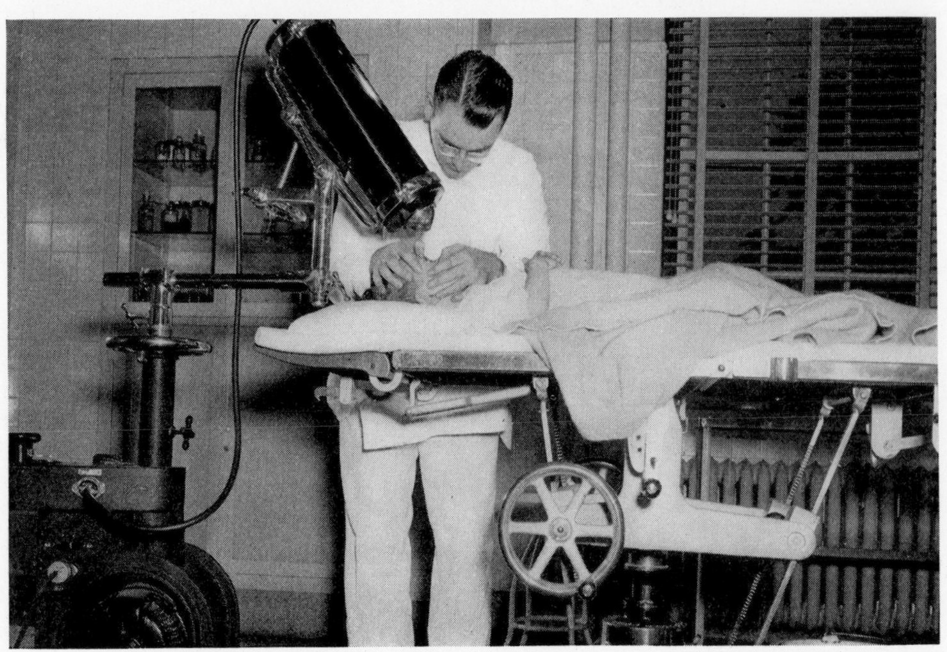

Eye magnet provided local hospitals takes care of emergency cases

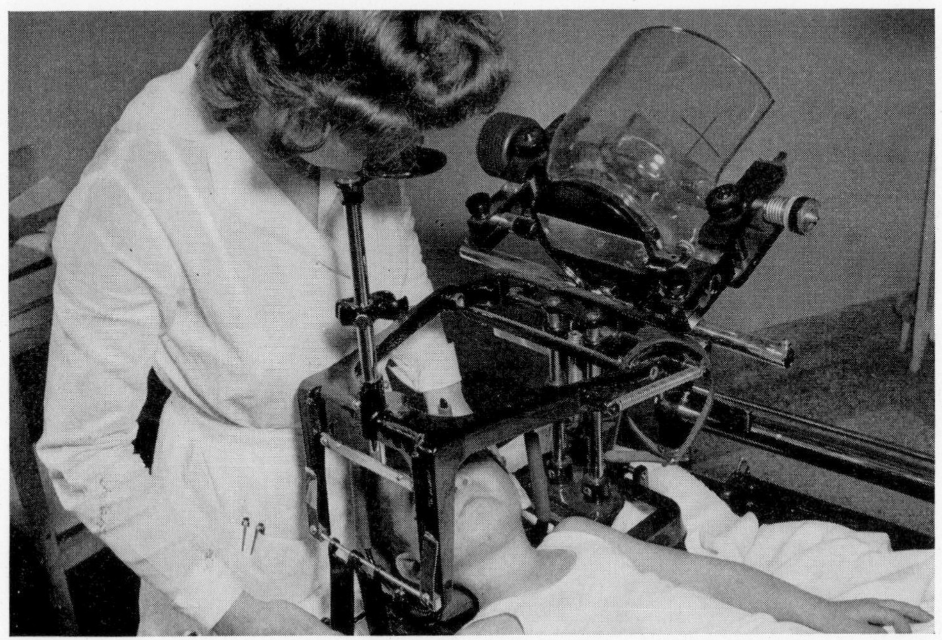

Research on diseases of the eye is financed by Foundation grant

Children's library of talking books developed experimentally by American Foundation for the Blind with Foundation aid

Visual hearing is taught children whose deafness is known to be progressive or permanent

Mental hygiene program is designed to reduce maladjustment, but retarded children and special cases are provided for

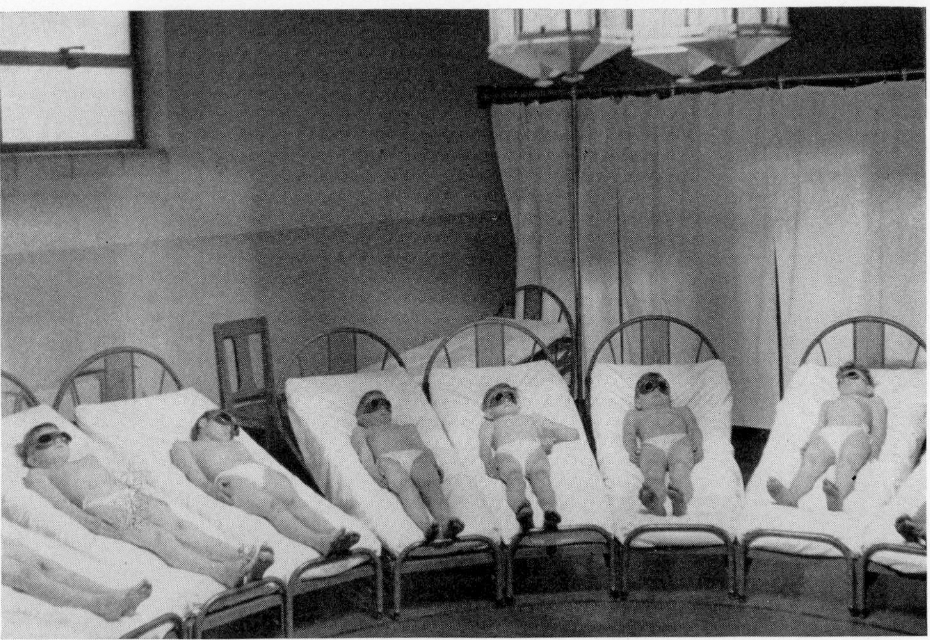

Special treatment under medical direction helps children with various handicaps including heart disease

Rheumatic fever, important cause of high mortality from heart disease, is investigated by Dr. A. F. Coburn at Columbia University

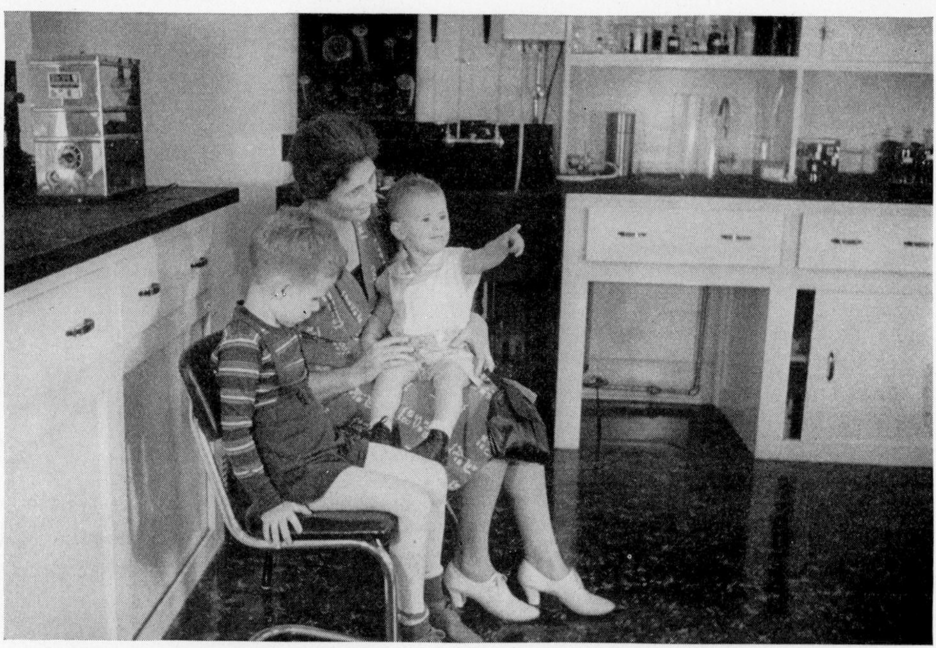

Diagnostic laboratories made possible by Foundation at request of county medical societies are boon to patients and physicians alike

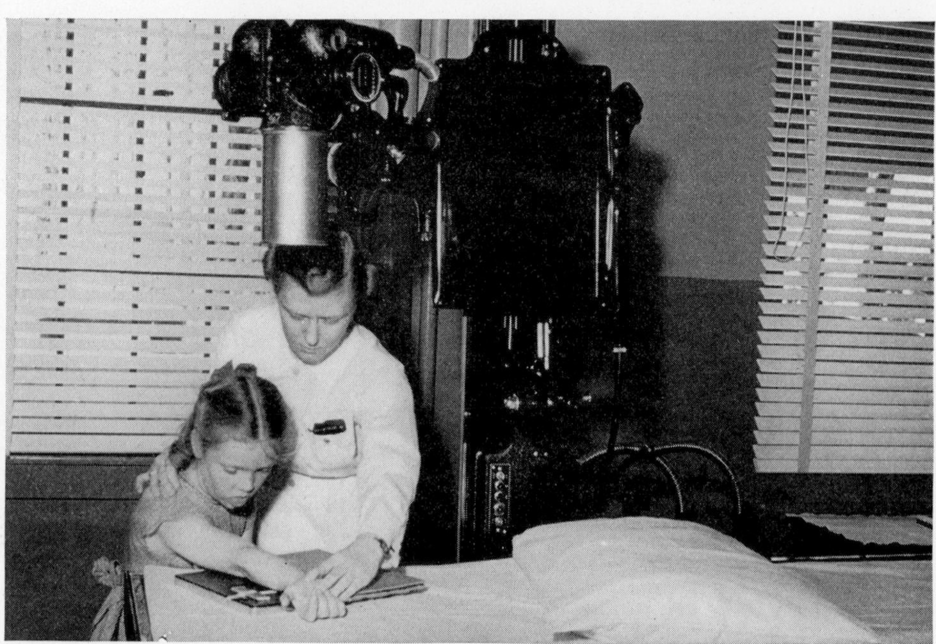

Greatly reduced fees dramatically increase number of clients and laboratories are self-supporting before end of 18 months

State Health Department and cooperating specialists supervise laboratories and provide regular consultant service

Experimental x-ray equipment is provided University of Michigan Hospital and California Institute of Technology

Prenatal and postnatal visits of public health nurses point to need for improved obstetrical care at time of delivery

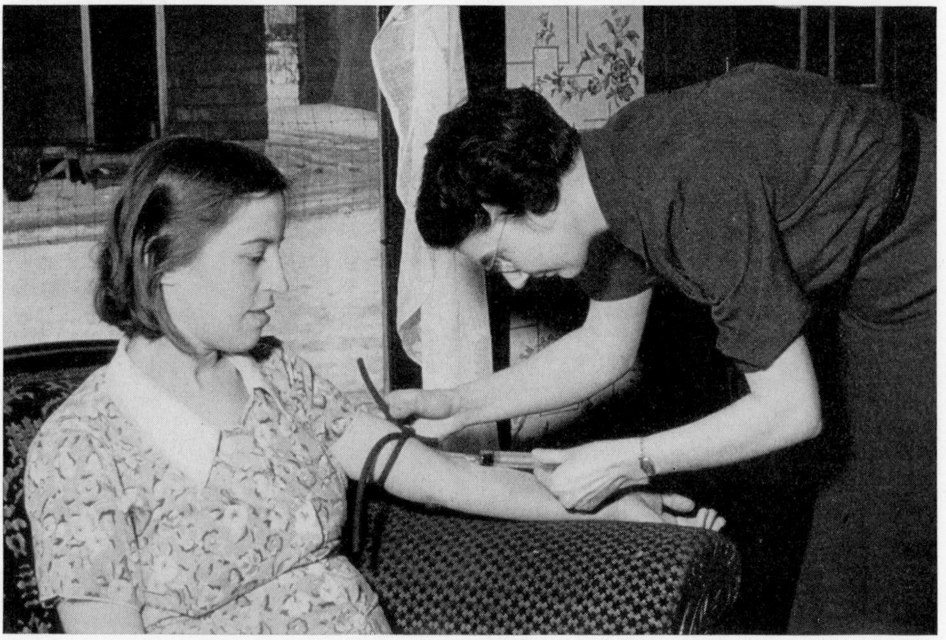

Research on the anemias of pregnancy is carried on by University of Michigan with Foundation aid

Foundation special consultants review a study of maternal and infant deaths in area and recommend a maternity nursing service

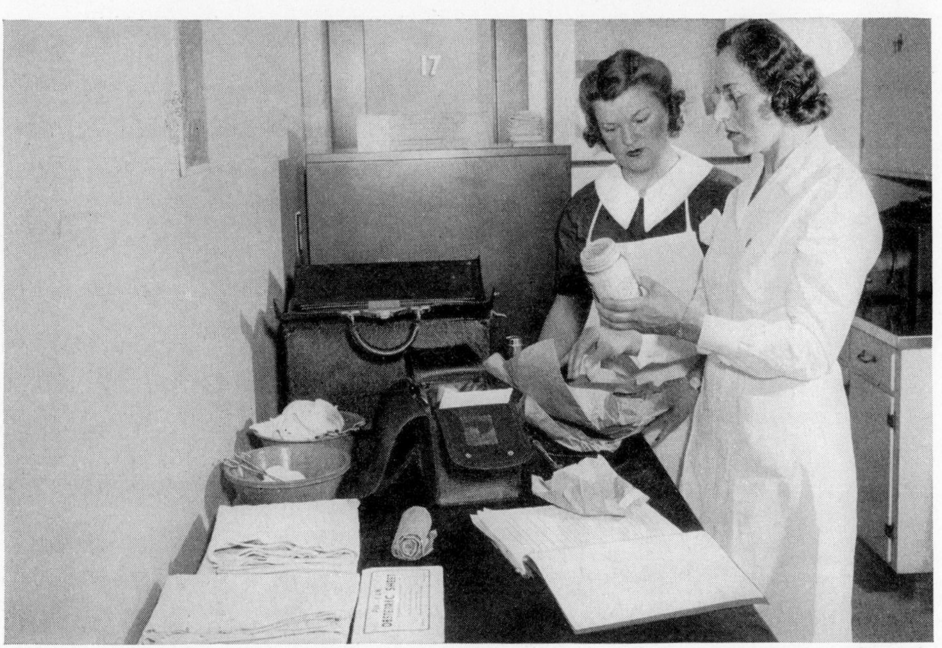

Maternity nurses receive intensive training in Chicago and Detroit in obstetrical nursing on Foundation scholarships

Community planning makes it possible for most mothers to have benefit of maternity nursing service either at home or hospital

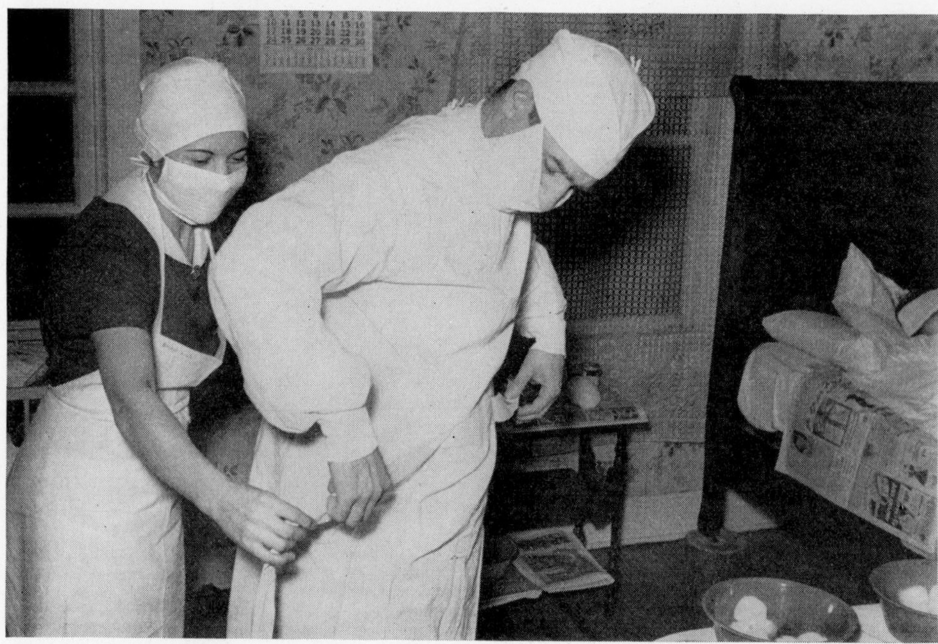

Maternity nurses assist the physicians at time of delivery in the home

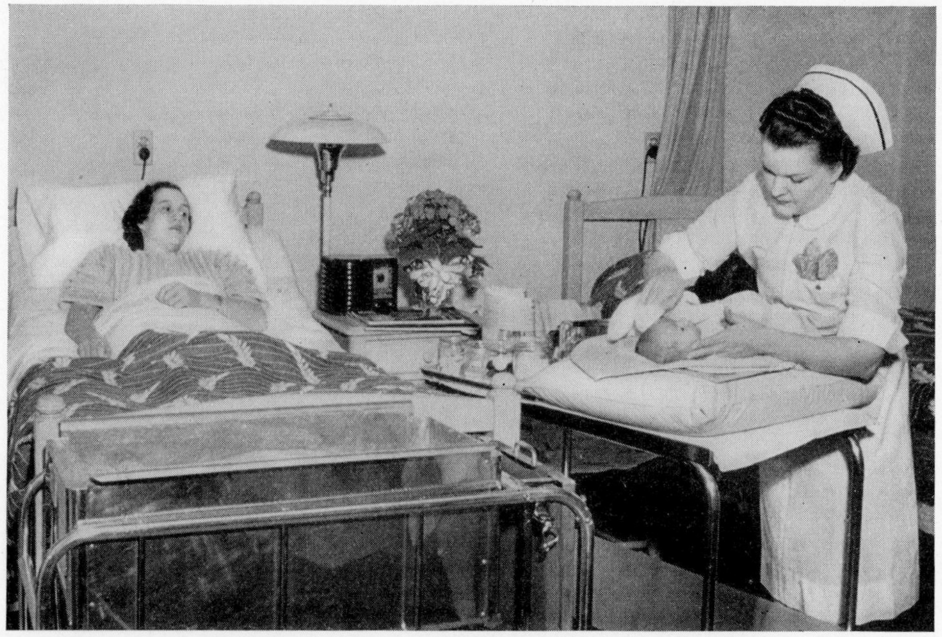

They provide the same service for mothers and new babies in the hospitals

Public health nurses take over instruction of mother and father a few days after delivery

Special consultant on maternity nursing provided by Foundation develops and maintains quality of nursing service

Children's Bureau and Foundation funds provide State Health Department with medical consultant for physicians and lay education

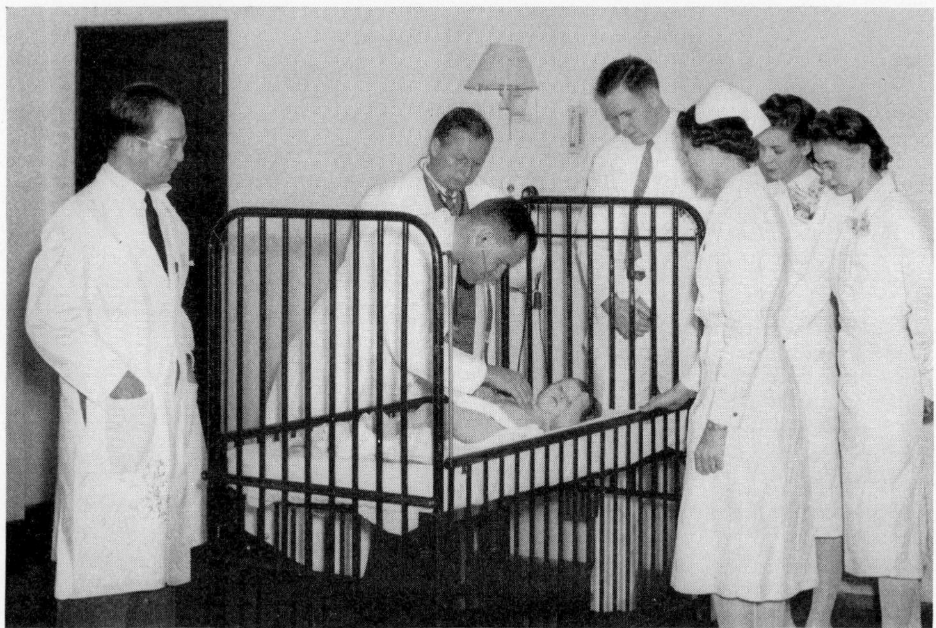

Department of Pediatrics of University of Michigan improves training of student, and graduate physician, with Foundation grant

Hospital nursing supervisors adopt uniform procedures and take special scholarships in obstetrics to better supervise service

Hospital administrators discuss needs for additional facilities with Foundation officials and prepare plans for new construction

City of Allegan builds 40-bed hospital assisted by grants from the P.W.A. and Foundation

City of Hillsdale replaces old hospital with modern 60-bed unit with P.W.A. and Foundation assistance

Branch County provides up-to-date facilities with construction of a 60-bed hospital under P.W.A. and Foundation programs

Construction continues with the erection of a new 40-bed hospital by City of South Haven with Foundation aid

City of Plainwell adds 15 beds and improved laboratory, operating, and delivery facilities to hospital with Foundation grant

City of Albion is helped to modernize its 45-bed hospital throughout

City of Hastings adds facilities for maternity patients and improves operating room with assistance from Foundation

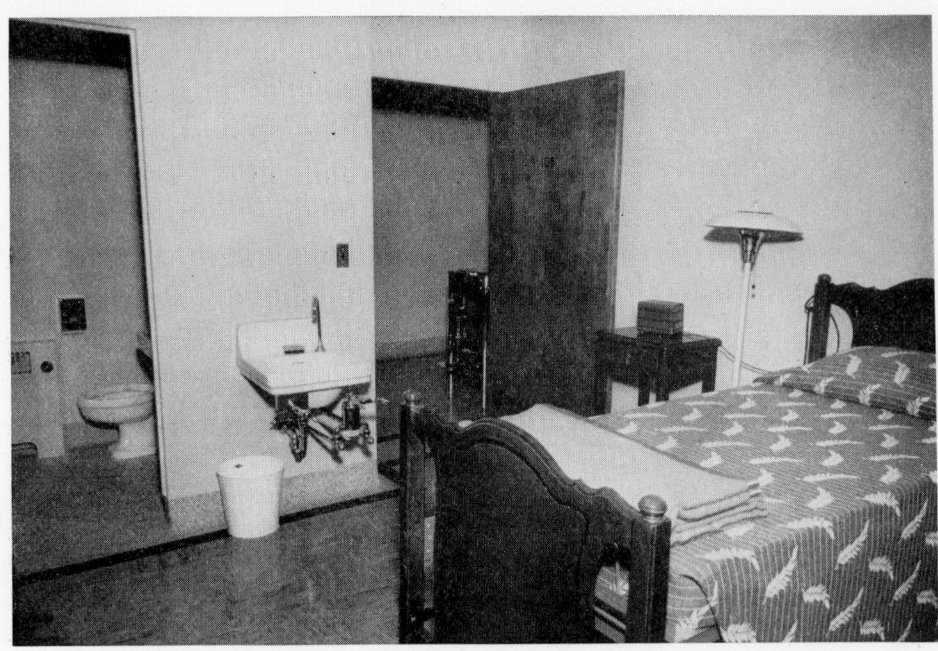

Light, cheerful rooms and good care change attitude of community toward hospital

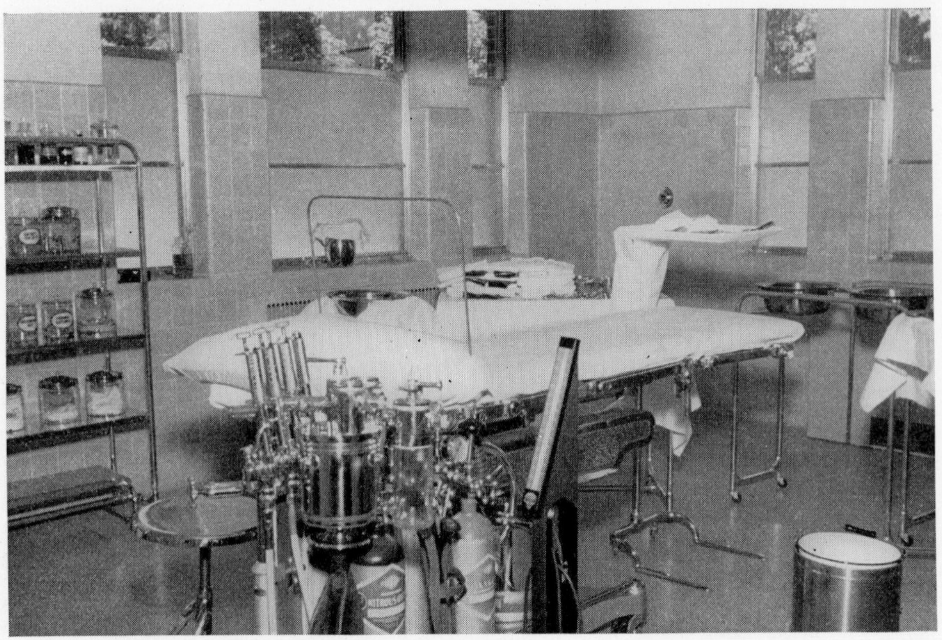

Up-to-date operating rooms and equipment help to provide best type of professional care for rural citizens

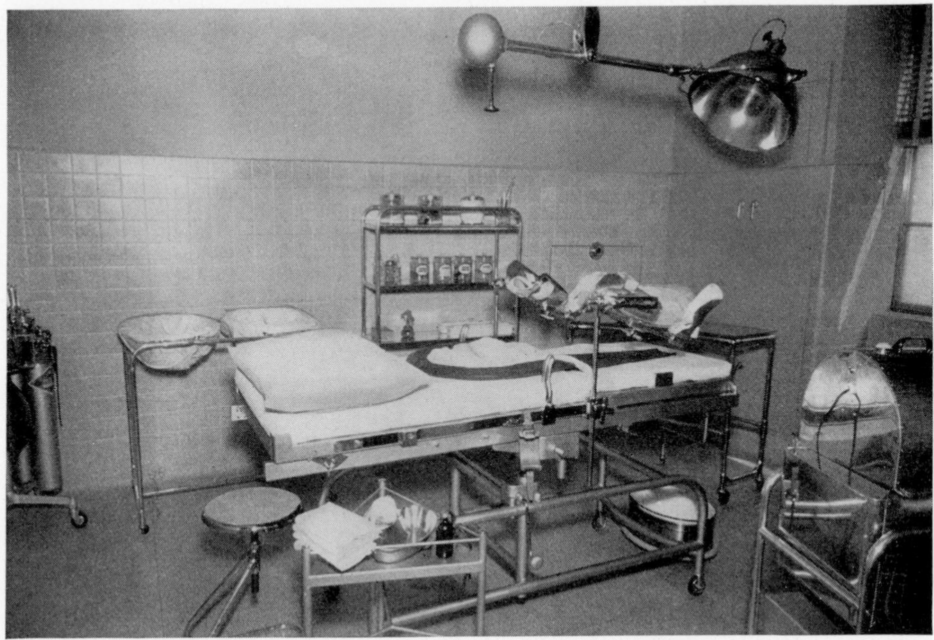

Modern service that protects against all emergencies increases use of hospitals when babies are born

Properly supervised diets and tasty foods add to effectiveness of medical treatment

Uniform accounting procedures in all hospitals give new cost analyses and improve operation

Hospital trustees study problems and responsibilities at University of Chicago on Foundation scholarships

Hospital auxiliaries study maternity nursing program and discuss possibilities of hourly nursing service

Pre-payment plans for rural citizens studied by hospital trustees

Ministers study "pastoral psychiatry" with Foundation aid and take active part in helping parishioners with life's problems

Newspaper editors request special course at Northwestern University on community problems and responsibilities of the press

Mothers ask for special courses on behavior problems of children at Merrill Palmer School in Detroit and University of Chicago

Fathers have short course too, on family and community problems at University of Chicago on Foundation scholarships

Township leaders organize "service clubs" and study local health and education needs at three-day institutes

Committee members develop "loan closets" of sick room equipment, and assist in preschool medical and dental programs

County supervisors request courses at University of Chicago and conduct educational poll of public opinion returning 68,000 ballots

Rural school board members visit modern schools as part of institutes at Universities of Chicago and Northwestern on school problems

Neglected rural schools present a new challenge to the local boards. They recognize the symptoms of decay of civic responsibility

Health department engineering records summarize the needs and point the way to a modernization program for hundreds of schools

County commissioners, school board members, and health departments plan improvement of building and accompanying education program

Tax history, school enrollment, preschool census, state aid, community trends, are weighed by supervisors in requesting Foundation aid

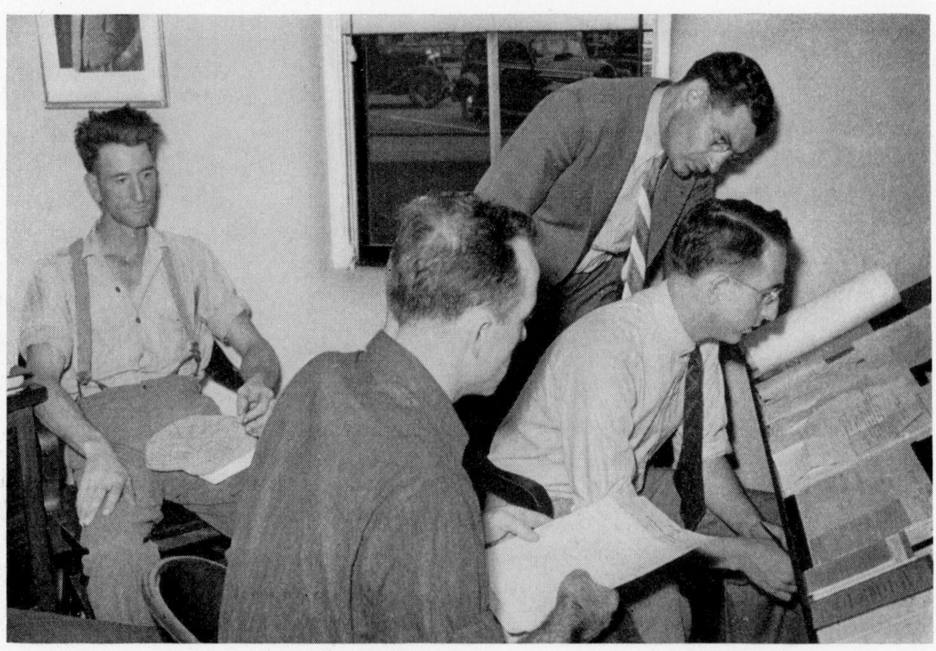

Local contractors and craftsmen are educated by cooperating in drawing specifications and maintaining standards in construction

Whole community is interested and many obtain data for similar improvements to water supply and sewage disposal systems for their farm homes

Buildings are remodeled to provide inside frost-proof toilets and level floors for movable furniture

Inexpensive pressure water systems provide convenient drinking water, hand-washing facilities, and flush toilets

More windows, electric lights, tilt-top tables improve reading conditions. Files house teaching aids and interlocking record system

Semi-automatic heating systems improve health, comfort. Movable furniture provides flexibility for instruction, games and meetings

5-year bond, 15 mill tax limit restricts consolidation, but Foundation aid permits some construction. Kellogg Agricultural School

Pittsford Consolidated School. 50% of rural youth ultimately migrate to urban centers. Educational problems recognize no boundaries

Delton Agricultural School. Bus routes with a maximum of nine miles reduce travel time to minimum

Level Park School. Suburban areas require special integration with larger school systems of adjacent cities

Nashville School. Consolidation is favored by high tax districts, opposed by low, reflecting taxpayer interest in education

Middleville Consolidated School. Consolidation supported only when new school tax does not exceed total of combined districts

Eaton Rapids School. Children with special needs can be more effectively provided for in larger school system

Mattawan Consolidated School. Additional agricultural training needed in rural areas is made available

Wayland Consolidated School. Consolidated schools stabilize rural districts, improve markets, property values

Olivet School. Larger schools provide socializing influences and extra-curricular activities important to maturing personalities

Woodland School. Educational opportunities are multiplied many times

Ann J. Kellogg School. Handicapped children enroll in "opportunity school" with 600 normal youngsters. Stigma is avoided

W. K. Kellogg Auditorium and Junior High School. Facilities of this school permit it to double as community center

Large community gatherings utilize auditorium for lectures, public debates, open forums, musical events and entertainments

Village superintendents take special courses and then study their schools in the light of modern educational objectives

Crowded village schools, many with out-of-date instructional materials and out-moded programs, present many problems

Village schools are modernized with Foundation grants in aid

Flexible equipment adapts itself easily to varied uses

School janitors take short courses at Michigan State College on school care and maintenance

Social life of rural communities centers around combination gymnasium and auditorium

Farm shops are important in rural agricultural schools

Modern equipment offers new opportunities for children and teachers

Student participation in school affairs develops problem-solving skills, social responsibility, cooperative attitudes

Civic responsibility may be a privilege we will fight to enjoy or a duty to dodge depending upon our early training and experience

Experimental studies in nutrition open up exciting new fields

Domestic science classes combine satisfactions of achievement with practical knowledge of food value, marketing, preparation

Dining room and kitchen equipment installed in many schools with Foundation assistance permits a practical approach to nutrition

Planning of balanced diets, proper service for social functions, vocational training, and restaurant management are studied

Business methods, school banks and school money, combined with proper selection of foods present many teaching opportunities

Many schools raise their own vegetables

Public health nurses carry instruction on meal planning and budget buying into homes

State health department consultant subsidized by Foundation advises public health nurses and teachers on nutritional problems

Hot lunch programs in rural schools provide an opportunity for comprehensive educational projects

Food purchasing committees demand high nourishing and protective values for their money and raise question of safety of food supplies

Children learn that when they buy milk it should be pasteurized and why

Milk producers and distributors work with health department to improve community milk supply

Veterinarians take short course scholarships at Cornell University and bring latest scientific procedures to dairy herd operators

Public health engineers and milk plant operators work together to improve quality and safeguard supply on the farm and in the plant

Veterinarians and physicians meet to coordinate plans for maintaining high standards for milk and food supplies

Milk producers and processors study bacteriological and chemical tests at Purdue University on Foundation scholarships

State Health Department, University of Michigan, Army Medical Corps, join Foundation in mock epidemic test of safeguards of food supplies

Thorough community organization of all responsible professional and lay groups is not too high a price to pay for protection of children

Public health engineers draw up plans for educational approach to other problems in the field of sanitation

Cooperative programs of resort owners and health department protect vacationists. Standards are high. Consultation available

Decentralization of industry makes industrial hygiene an important part of duties of public health engineers

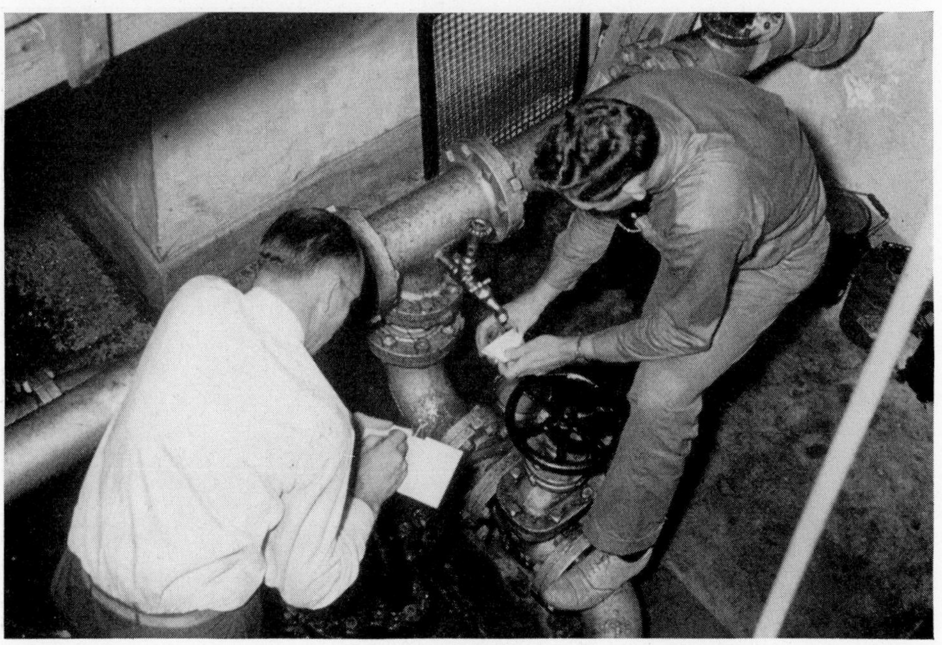

School, municipal, home water supplies are checked by public health engineers for purity and dangerous cross-connections

Out-of-school farm boys and girls are eligible for scholarships for concentrated eight-week courses at Michigan State College

Problems found by survey of students' own farms form basis of instruction in which health department personnel takes part

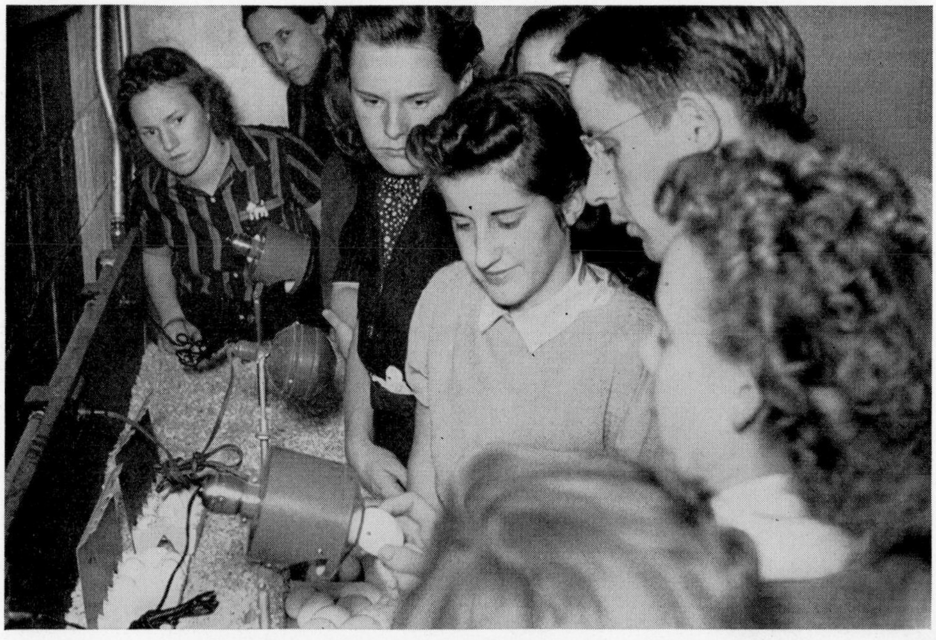

Farm management, dairying, crop rotation, community resources, home making, child care, all have a place in the course

Course director follows graduates into the field with practical advice. County agricultural agents have important roles

Short course graduates provide active leadership. Future Farmers and 4-H clubs given loan funds with which children buy farm stock

Institutes and short courses are provided for recreation leaders. Teachers and mothers learn games for children

Foundation makes camp facilities available to American Red Cross for training waterfront leaders and lifeguards

American Camping Association and Foundation jointly sponsor national workshops on camping programs and management

Youth organizations such as Boy Scouts and Camp Fire Girls receive Foundation assistance in leadership training and camping programs

W. K. K. F. Pine Lake Camp School is operated the year round for children from all over state of Michigan

W. K. K. F. Clear Lake Camp School. These camps accommodate 50 children in winter and 165 in cabins in summer

W. K. K. F. St. Mary's Lake Camp School. The camps are used for many different types of programs for child and adult groups

Constructive influence of out-of-door activity helps underprivileged and exceptional children alike

Capable teachers staff the camps. Often rural children and their teachers come for two weeks to live and work together

Health is improved, habits and attitudes are changed, friendships developed, confidence gained, and new interests found

The camps are also used for mothers' institutes, three-day meetings of teachers, health department staffs, and many other adult groups

Social agencies like the Michigan Children's Aid Society are assisted with boarding care and in developing professional staffs

Law enforcement officers request short courses on methods of handling juvenile delinquency

Starr Commonwealth for pre-delinquent boys is aided with medical and dental programs and a pasteurizing and bottling plant

Assistance for playgrounds and playground supervision helps to promote positive recreational programs and reduce delinquency

Battle Creek recreational programs center around W. K. K. F. Youth Building operated by the city under a Foundation grant

Several hundred different individuals use Youth Building daily, including many soldiers from nearby Fort Custer

Thousands of children learn to swim and national champions have been developed in pools built and subsidized by Foundation

Sports develop community interest among spectators as well as participants

Foundation library serves all professional people in seven counties. A post card will bring the book by return mail

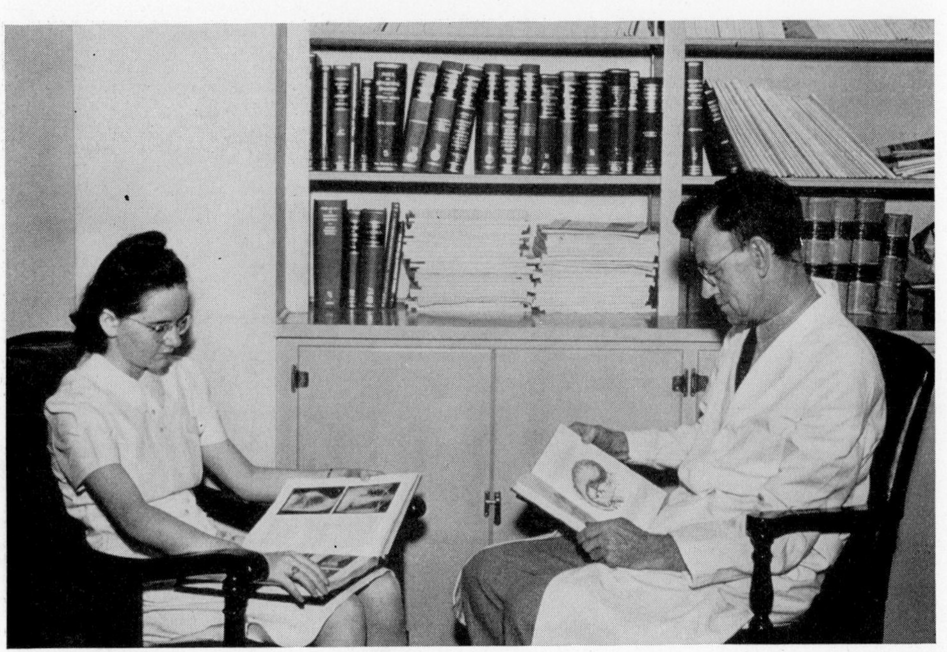

Special collections are loaned to hospitals, libraries and schools

Library trustees, public and school librarians take short courses on Foundation scholarships

Library problems are studied at three-day librarian encampment at St. Mary's Lake Camp

Potential power of rural, village and school libraries contrasts sharply with neglected quarters and dormant programs

Experimental loans, first of 1,800, later 18,000, children's books by Foundation stimulate local committees to plan library program

Ten-day campaigns bring out old books from schools, libraries and homes. Lists are checked and valuable editions returned

Library days celebrate collection of 900,000 outworn volumes. Foundation grants provide new book for every five turned in

Book fairs are held. Consultants help teachers, librarians, and children's committees select new books from comprehensive exhibits

Circulation figures in school libraries increase dramatically as new reading interests are discovered by hundreds of children

Village libraries have authors' teas and story hours. Reading circles are formed. Books are served, not preserved

Every rural school has book corner. Collections are exchanged cooperatively under a county master plan. Parents like the books too

All of these different activities arouse the interest of leaders from near and far. South American visitors study the project

40 *professional schools and universities send students for field experience. Faculty members visit the area and review work*

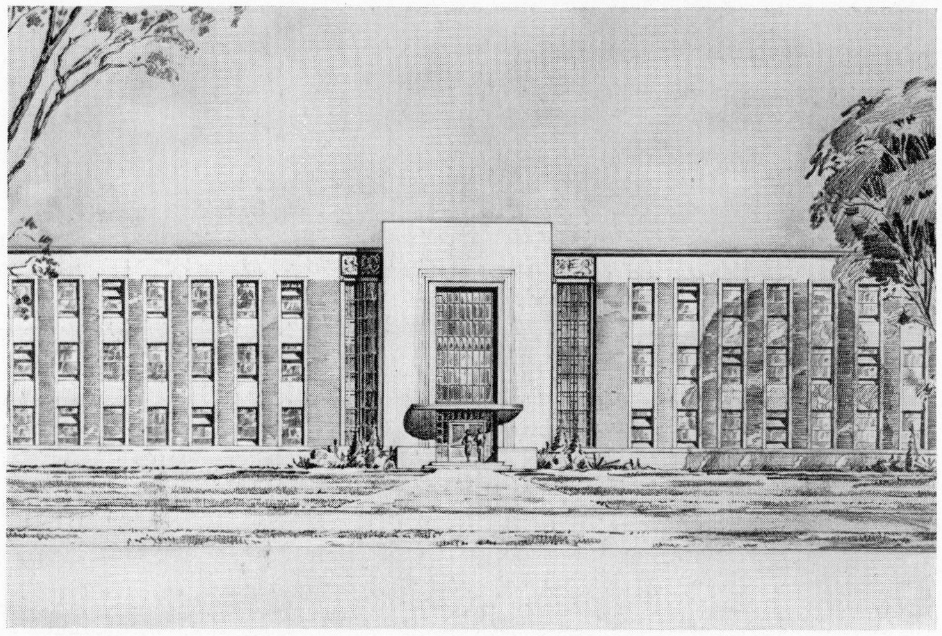

New University of Michigan School of Public Health financed by W. K. Kellogg and Rockefeller Foundations meets postgraduate needs

Public health engineering fellows in 1940 came from 25 universities throughout the country

Students get first-hand knowledge of health departments and are assigned real jobs

They make their first mistakes under supervision

Students make home calls and get acquainted with the human factors that operate in all equations

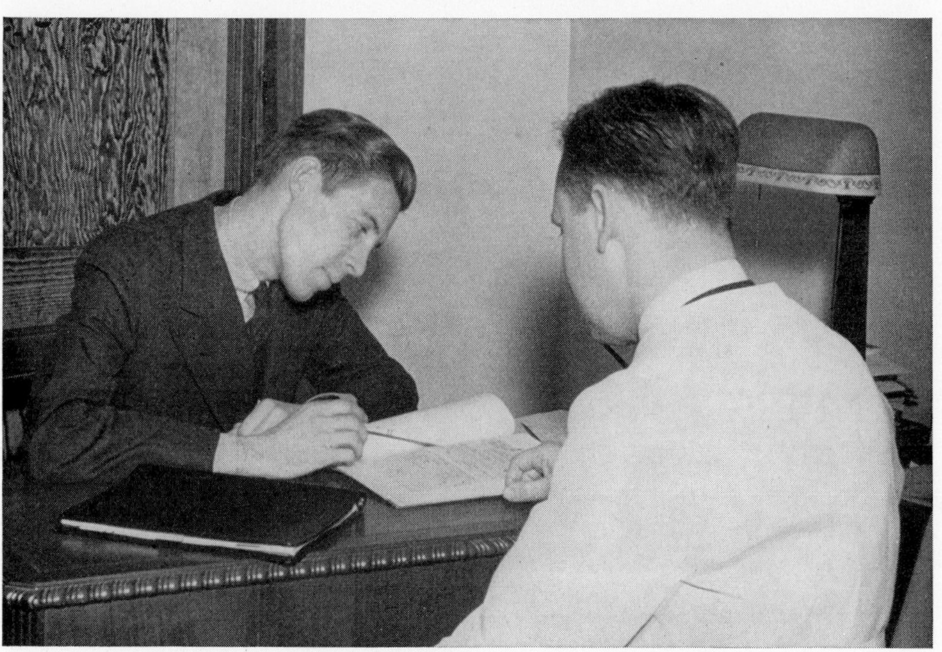

Medical students spend time with physicians, dental students with dentists. They see community program from inside

Students discuss community problems with school commissioners and other leaders

They participate in meetings of medical, dental, educational societies and lay groups

Students share their experiences with each other at regular committee meetings with Foundation consultants

Fellowship and understanding grow with exchange of experience between areas and between generations. Mr. Kellogg talks to students

REPORT OF THE TREASURER

REPORT OF THE TREASURER

THE W. K. Kellogg Foundation is a Michigan corporation, incorporated on June 20, 1930, under the provisions of Part 1, Chapter 1, Section 2, of Act No. 84 of the Public Acts of Michigan for 1921 (but now operating under Act. No. 327 of the Public Acts of Michigan for 1931 as amended) providing for the organization, regulation, and classification of domestic corporations.

The affairs of the corporation are administered by a board of nine trustees elected from the membership of the corporation. The members are elected for a three-year term, and the terms overlap so that not more than one-third of the terms expire in any one fiscal year. The Articles of Association and the By-Laws of the corporation as now in force will be found in the appendix.

The Foundation is the beneficiary of a trust created by Mr. W. K. Kellogg, of which the Harris Trust and Savings Bank of Chicago, Illinois, is the corporate trustee, and Glenn A. Cross, George B. Darling, and Emory W. Morris, of Battle Creek, Michigan, are co-trustees. The distribution clause of this trust instrument and a synopsis of certain other sections of the trust will be found in the appendix. The assets of the trust consist of over 50% of the common stock of the Kellogg Company. The trustees have the responsibility of determining at regular intervals whether the affairs of the W. K. Kellogg Foundation have been conducted in accordance with the provisions of the trust instrument.

Such general fund assets as the Foundation may have for investment are invested by a Finance Committee of four members elected by the Board from its members. This committee is empowered to secure such advice and counsel as it deems necessary for the safe investment of funds appropriated by the Board of Trustees for investment.

Not more than four of the executive officers of the Foundation may be members of the Board of Trustees. The President and the General Director administer the programs adopted and supervise the expenditures made by the Board of Trustees. The President and the General Director are assisted by a staff of directors and consultants who not only provide consultative service to the Michigan Community Health Project, but assume responsibility for such field programs as may be assigned to them from time to time.

The Board of Trustees appoints for one-year terms special consultants in special fields who are available to the administrative officers of the Foundation for such consultative service as they may deem desirable.

In this, the first published report of the W. K. Kellogg Foundation, it has been deemed appropriate to include statements pertaining to the first ten years of the Foundation's operations, as well as statements for the fiscal year ended August 31, 1941.

The combined balance sheets, Exhibit I and Exhibit A, include the accounts of the W. K. Kellogg Foundation and the accounts of the W. K. Kellogg Foundation Trust. It has been considered desirable to include the accounts of the Foundation Trust, inasmuch as the relationship between the Foundation and the Foundation Trust is such that a balance sheet of the Foundation alone would not present a complete statement of the assets, the principal or income from which are available for the purposes for which the Foundation was founded. The remaining exhibits, however, refer to the accounts and operations of the W. K. Kellogg Foundation alone. Income received by the W. K. Kellogg Foundation Trust is paid over to the Foundation after deductions or reserves for trustees' fees and trust expenses.

The accounts of the Foundation are maintained on the basis of cash receipts and disbursements, except in respect of expenditure commitments, amortization of premiums on investments, and provision for depreciation of real estate and equipment. Therefore, the accompanying financial statements do not reflect income accrued but not received nor liabilities incurred but not paid. It has been the general policy of the Board of Trustees to pay grants in their entirety at the time they are approved by the Board of Trustees, even though expenditure is intended to be made over a period of years.

As shown by Exhibit A (the combined balance sheet of the W. K. Kellogg Foundation and of the W. K. Kellogg Foundation Trust), the total assets at August 31, 1941 were $46,574,167.69. The W. K. Kellogg Foundation Trust Fund Securities represent $31,970,000 of this amount (stated at estimated value as at the several dates of receipt from Founder) and the remainder, or $14,604,167.69, is represented by the general fund assets. The main sources of the general fund assets have been from gifts received directly or indirectly from Mr. Kellogg and from the excess of income over expenses.

At August 31, 1941, cash and securities represented over 85% of the general fund assets. Cash in banks and on hand totaled $947,274.78, including $35,398.15 held by the corporate trustee of the W. K. Kellogg Foundation Trust.

A complete list of the security holdings at August 31, 1941 is presented in Exhibit F. The approximate quoted market values are shown in this exhibit as well as the ledger or carrying values. The investment policy of the Foundation, which is determined primarily by its Finance Committee, must obviously give consideration to annual program requirements as well as the customary attention to security and yield. As mentioned heretofore, the Foundation observes the conservative policy of amortizing the premiums on investments. Exhibit G sets forth the transactions in respect of securities purchased, exchanged, sold or redeemed during the year ended August 31, 1941. The majority of the Foundation's security holdings are in the custody of the Harris Trust and Savings Bank.

Other general fund assets include certain notes and mortgages received as gifts which are being gradually liquidated. Among the assets given directly or indirectly to the Foundation by Mr. Kellogg have been several pieces of real estate in and about Battle Creek, including the Kellogg Inn Company, now known as Atlas Properties, Incorporated (the Foundation owning all of the capital stock of this corporation). Most of the real estate holdings of the Foundation in and about Battle Creek, not useful in connection with its programs, have been transferred to Atlas Properties, Incorporated, for the purpose of operation and liquidation, and Atlas Properties, Incorporated, gave the Foundation its notes in settlement. As the properties are liquidated payments are made upon these notes. Since the Foundation has not followed a policy of purchasing real estate as an investment, most of the real estate once owned by it has been liquidated, and today the principal real estate holding of Atlas Properties, Incorporated, is the Kellogg Inn, an apartment building in Battle Creek in which the Foundation has two floors for offices.

The real estate and equipment shown on the accompanying combined balance sheet, Exhibit A, falls into two general categories. In the first category are those properties, such as the Pine, Clear and St. Mary's Lake Camps and the Youth Building in Battle Creek, which are related to the program of the Foundation and are operated or subsidized by it as part of that program. These properties, together with the office furniture and equipment used in the Foundation's general offices, are considered subject to depreciation in a manner consistent with sound business practice. The other class of properties, included in the accompanying combined balance sheet, represent certain other real estate holdings received as gifts by the Foundation. These latter properties are operated for the most part by Atlas Properties, Incorporated.

Exhibit II and Exhibit C show the particulars of cash receipts and disbursements for the period from the inception of the Foundation on June 20, 1930 to August 31, 1940, and for the fiscal year ended August 31, 1941, respectively. It will be seen from these exhibits that the major sources of income have been the income from the W. K. Kellogg Foundation Trust, and other trusts which are no longer in existence, and from stocks, bonds and other securities owned directly by the Foundation. Except for amounts disbursed in connection with the purchase of investments, the major item of disbursements has been in respect of expenditures, the details of which are set forth on Exhibit III and Exhibits D and E.

In considering the administrative and general expenditures, as shown by Exhibit III and Exhibit D, it should be noted that there are included therein the amounts expended on the so-called security program of the Foundation, which embraces the consultants, the staffs of the central office, of the county health departments of the Michigan Community Health Project, and of Pine, Clear and St. Mary's Lake Camps. The Board of Trustees, recognizing that the persons on these staffs were not eligible for the usual social security benefits provided by law, deemed it desirable that a security program be developed for them, the expense of which would be borne by the Foundation. The program now in effect includes group life and retirement income insurance, medical care, hospital care, and permanent disability benefits. In addition, in order to provide the professional members of the staffs with an opportunity for continued education and to assure a continuity of staff at all times, provision is made for sabbatical leaves for study at prescribed intervals. The entire cost of this program, which is borne by the Foundation, is shown as a general expenditure and no attempt is made to prorate it on the basis of the various groups benefited.

Respectfully submitted,
EMORY W. MORRIS, *Treasurer.*

To the Board of Trustees,

W. K. Kellogg Foundation:

We have examined the books and accounts of W. K. Kellogg Foundation and the exhibits contained in the Treasurer's report for the year ended August 31, 1941. The accounts of the W. K. Kellogg Foundation Trust (consisting of the W. K. Kellogg Foundation Trust Fund Securities and cash balances of $25,594.05 and $35,398.15 at August 31, 1940, and at August 31, 1941, respectively) are kept by the Harris Trust and Savings Bank, the Corporate Trustee. We have not examined these accounts but have received each year direct from the Corporate Trustee a confirmation as to the securities and cash held by them for the W. K. Kellogg Foundation Trust. The income receivable on the W. K. Kellogg Foundation Trust Fund Securities has been accounted for by confirmations received direct from the Kellogg Company.

With regard to our examination of the accounts of the Foundation, the cash and security investments at August 31, 1941, were confirmed by certificates obtained from the depositaries or by inspection. The balances receivable on accounts, notes and mortgages were confirmed direct to us by the respective debtors. We have reviewed in detail the transactions for the year and have satisfied ourselves by examination of accounting records of the Foundation and other supporting evidence that the income from investments and other cash receipts were properly accounted for and that expenditures and security investment transactions were duly authorized and supported by proper vouchers. We have made similar examinations annually since the inception of the Foundation.

The accounts of the Foundation are maintained on the basis of cash receipts and disbursements, except in respect of expenditure commitments, amortization of premiums on investments, and provision for depreciation of real estate and equipment.

In our opinion, the accompanying balance sheets and the related exhibits present fairly the combined position of the W. K. Kellogg Foundation and the W. K. Kellogg Foundation Trust at August 31, 1940 and at August 31, 1941, and the transactions of the W. K. Kellogg Foundation for the period from inception on June 20, 1930 to August 31, 1940 and for the year ended August 31, 1941.

Price, Waterhouse & Co.

Detroit, October 15, 1941.

TABLE OF CONTENTS

Exhibit I

W. K. KELLOGG FOUNDATION

AND

W. K. KELLOGG FOUNDATION TRUST

COMBINED BALANCE SHEET—AUGUST 31, 1940

ASSETS

GENERAL FUND:			
Cash in Banks and on Hand			
Cash balance W. K. Kellogg Foundation (Exhibit II)		$915,093.94	
Cash held by W. K. Kellogg Foundation Trust . .		25,594.05	$ 940,687.99
Securities, at estimated values as at dates of receipt from donors or at cost to the Foundation, less amortization of premiums			11,252,813.07
Other Assets			
Accounts receivable		$ 3,925.00	
Notes receivable (at face amounts)—			
Atlas Properties, Incorporated . .	$674,998.00		
Others	152,700.00	827,698.00	
Mortgages receivable (at face amounts)		324,504.23	
Life insurance policies		135,708.32	
Claim against closed bank		76,493.15	
Real estate and equipment (at values set up at date of receipt from donors or at cost to the Foundation, less accumulated depreciation from date of acquisition)		790,830.89	
Advances to pay Federal income taxes assessed in respect of income paid W. K. Kellogg Foundation from certain trusts, for which taxes claims for refund have been made	$869,503.07		
Payments of Federal excise taxes on dividends for which claims for refund have been made	126,840.00		
Together (per contra)		996,343.07	3,155,502.66
Total General Fund			$15,349,003.72
W. K. KELLOGG FOUNDATION TRUST FUND			
1,105,000 shares of common stock of Kellogg Company (stated at estimated value as at the several dates of receipt from Founder)			31,970,000.00
			$47,319,003.72

Exhibit I

W. K. KELLOGG FOUNDATION

AND

W. K. KELLOGG FOUNDATION TRUST

COMBINED BALANCE SHEET—AUGUST 31, 1940

LIABILITIES

GENERAL FUND:		
Amounts provided for 1940–41 expenditures		$ 2,553,650.00
Amounts provided for expenditures to be made subsequent to August 31, 1941		120,800.00
Amounts provided in prior years as follows—		
For advances to pay Federal income taxes assessed in respect of income paid W. K. Kellogg Foundation from certain trusts, for which taxes claims for refund have been made	$869,503.07	
For Federal excise taxes on dividends for which claims for refund have been made	126,840.00	
Together (per contra)	$996,343.07	
For interest on excise taxes on dividends	15,000.00	1,011,343.07
General Fund Balance as at August 31, 1940		11,663,210.65
Total General Fund		$15,349,003.72
W. K. KELLOGG FOUNDATION TRUST FUND .		31,970,000.00
		$47,319,003.72

Exhibit II

W. K. KELLOGG FOUNDATION

STATEMENT OF RECEIPTS AND DISBURSEMENTS

JUNE 20, 1930 THROUGH AUGUST 31, 1940

RECEIPTS:		
Income		*Amount*
W. K. Kellogg Foundation Trust and other trusts		$16,708,636.26
Dividends received on stocks owned		1,042,503.84
Dividends received on insurance policies		5,935.50
Interest received—		
On bonds	$ 946,529.49	
On other securities	135,813.61	1,082,343.10
Rental income from properties		21,778.62
Total income		$18,861,197.32
Gifts		
Founder	$ 949,998.22	
Fellowship Corporation	38,231.32	
Others	135,886.65	1,124,116.19
Other		
Proceeds from securities sold, matured or redeemed	$ 5,385,069.95	
Collections on notes, mortgages and land contracts	140,822.70	
Repayment of advances by the Board of Education of City of Battle Creek, Michigan	92,000.00	
Advance by Founder	100,000.00	
Recoveries from closed bank	137,644.99	
Miscellaneous receipts	9,024.45	5,864,562.09
Total		$25,849,875.60
DEDUCT—DISBURSEMENTS:		
Expenditures (Exhibit III)	$ 8,228,018.95	
Cash in closed bank	214,138.14	
Advances to pay Federal income taxes assessed in respect of income paid W. K. Kellogg Foundation from certain trusts, for which taxes claims for refund have been made	869,503.07	
Purchase of furnishings and equipment of the Kellogg Inn and Hotel	40,490.13	
Advance to the Board of Education of City of Battle Creek, Michigan	92,000.00	
Repayment of advance made by Founder	100,000.00	
Operation of certain properties	125,390.39	
Purchase of investments	15,264,476.73	
Miscellaneous disbursements	764.25	24,934,781.66
Cash in Banks and on Hand as at August 31, 1940		$ 915,093.94

EXHIBIT III

W. K. KELLOGG FOUNDATION

STATEMENT OF EXPENDITURES

JUNE 20, 1930 THROUGH AUGUST 31, 1940

ADMINISTRATION AND GENERAL		
ADMINISTRATION		
Salaries	$ 356,174.38	
Travel	29,684.10	
Honoraria to Trustees	6,656.21	
Rent and light	44,812.64	
Legal services and expenses	35,853.57	
Telephone and telegraph	22,232.13	
Auditing	22,471.29	
Insurance—general	9,629.00	
Office furniture and equipment	46,651.39	
Postage and express	5,936.79	
Stationery and office supplies	13,841.50	
Documentary stamps and transfer tax	7,084.47	
Miscellaneous	26,574.56	
Total	$ 627,602.03	
GENERAL		
Investment counsel and safekeeping of securities	$ 88,279.86	
Insurance		
Group life	11,745.68*	
Retirement income	95,119.99*	
Study leave	6,974.09*	
Health service	13,209.93*	
Disability benefits	558.87*	
Total	$ 215,888.42	
TOTAL ADMINISTRATION AND GENERAL		$ 843,490.45

*These items include payments for the staffs of the central office, the consultants, the county health departments of the Michigan Community Health Project, and Clear, Pine and St. Mary's Lake Camps.

Exhibit III (Continued)

GRANTS

International

American Public Health Association		
To conduct an annual rural health conservation contest for all full-time county and district health departments in the United States and Canada. 1934–1940, inclusive	$ 101,250.00	
Tomesti Health District, Roumania		
For the development of a nutritional program for school children. 1937	1,000.00	
World Federation of Education Associations		
For a secretariat to facilitate international exchange of health education materials. 1937–1940, inclusive	17,500.00	
Total International Grants		119,750.00

National

American Public Health Association		
For epidemiological studies concerning the control of communicable disease. 1936–1940, inclusive	52,405.50	
California Institute of Technology		
For the production and measurement of radioactive products and their application to treatment. 1940	8,000.00	
Columbia University		
College of Physicians and Surgeons		
For research on the causes, the methods of prevention and treatment of rheumatic fever in children. 1932–1939, inclusive	90,600.00	
Eye and Ear Research Fund, Inc., Chicago, Illinois		
For research on glaucoma, transplantation of the cornea in children, and influence of vitamins on ocular deficiencies. 1940	4,600.00	
Kanavel, Allen B., M.D., of the Dept. of Surgical Research of Northwestern University		
Research in congenital malformation of children's hands and feet. 1933	1,500.00	
National Society for the Prevention of Blindness		
For the prevention of blindness and the conservation of vision. 1933, '35, '36, '37, '39, and '40	1,000.00	
Total National Grants		158,105.50

STATE		
Cass County, Michigan		
To assist in establishing a county health department. 1940	1,000.00	
City of Detroit		
Department of Health		
For research on scarlet fever. 1934 and 1935	8,356.85	
Toward a tuberculosis control program. 1937	1,300.00	
Michigan State Department of Health		
Bureau of Maternal Hygiene		
For consultant service in obstetrics for practicing physicians. 1939 and 1940	7,083.32	
Michigan Infantile Paralysis Commission and Michigan Poliomyelitis Commission		
For consultant service in Michigan for the diagnosis and treatment of infantile paralysis in children. 1931 and 1939	6,000.00	
University of Michigan		
School of Dentistry		
For the enlargement of the faculty to provide graduate and postgraduate courses for practicing dentists. 1937–40, inclusive	70,000.00	
Toward the construction and equipment of a building for postgraduate and graduate dental study. 1939	256,500.00	
School of Medicine		
For field research on the anemias of pregnancy. 1939 and 1940	14,550.00	
For special equipment for making routine photoroentgenograms of all patients admitted to University Hospital. 1940	10,850.00	
University of Michigan and the Michigan Joint Committee on Health Education		
For public education in health and hygiene. 1936–40, inclusive	19,000.00	
Palo School, Palo, Ionia County, Michigan		
Toward construction of an addition to school building. 1934	3,335.92	
St. Joseph County, Michigan		
To assist in establishing a county health department. 1939	2,000.00	
Wayne University		
For instruction in preventive medicine and public health. 1938 and 1939	2,525.00	
Western State Teachers College		
For special equipment for diagnosis and treatment of speech defects in children. 1940	1,200.00	
TOTAL STATE GRANTS		403,701.09

Exhibit III (Continued)

GRANTS (Continued)

Michigan Community Health Project

Schools

Delta School, Delta, Eaton County, Michigan Toward the construction and equipment of an addition to school building. 1938	$ 9,350.00
Delton W. K. Kellogg Agricultural School, Delton, Barry County, Michigan Toward the construction and equipment of a consolidated rural agricultural school building. 1936	39,517.28
Eaton Rapids School, Eaton Rapids, Eaton County, Michigan Toward the construction and equipment of an elementary school building. 1939	75,000.00
W. K. Kellogg Agricultural School, Ross Township, Kalamazoo County, Michigan Toward the construction and equipment of a consolidated rural agricultural school building. 1931, '32, '36, '38, and '39	89,254.36
Level Park School, Calhoun County, Michigan Toward the construction and equipment of an addition to school building. 1938 and '39	25,000.00
Local School Boards in Van Buren and Branch Counties, Michigan For assistance in modernizing rural and village schools	102,785.93
Martin School, Martin, Allegan County, Mich. Toward the construction and equipment of an addition to school building. 1938	11,200.00
Mattawan Consolidated School, Mattawan, Van Buren County, Michigan Toward the construction and equipment of an addition to school building. 1939	21,000.00
Nashville W. K. Kellogg School, Nashville, Barry County, Michigan Toward the construction of an elementary and high school building. 1934, '36, and '37	35,732.58
Pittsford Rural Agricultural School, Pittsford, Hillsdale County, Michigan Toward the construction and equipment of a consolidated rural agricultural school building. 1939 and 1940	85,467.69

GRANTS (Continued) EXHIBIT III (Continued)

MICHIGAN COMMUNITY HEALTH PROJECT (Continued)

Schools (Continued)

Sunfield Public School, Sunfield, Eaton County, Michigan		
Toward the construction of home-making room and installation of plumbing equipment. 1940 .	$ 2,033.04	
Thornapple W. K. Kellogg Consolidated School, Middleville, Barry County, Michigan		
Toward the construction and equipment of consolidated rural agricultural school building. 1931, '32, '36, '37, and '40	144,932.82	
Walton Township Unit School, Olivet, Eaton County, Michigan		
Toward the construction and equipment of a consolidated rural agricultural school building. 1934, '36, '37, and '39	74,680.50	
Wattles Park School, Calhoun County, Michigan		
For furniture for new school building. 1940 . .	3,000.00	
Wayland Union School, Wayland, Allegan County, Michigan		
Toward the construction of a consolidated rural agricultural school building. 1940 . . .	50,000.00	
Woodland Township School, Woodland, Barry County, Michigan		
Toward the construction and equipment of a township unit consolidated school building. 1934, '36, and '37	50,849.08	
Total School Grants	$819,803.28	
Hospitals		
City of Allegan, Allegan County, Michigan		
Toward the construction and equipment of a forty-bed hospital building. 1939 and 1940. .	108,299.45	
County of Branch, Michigan		
Toward the construction and equipment of a sixty-bed hospital. 1939 and 1940.	120,773.85	
City of Hillsdale, Hillsdale County, Michigan		
Toward the construction and equipment of a sixty-bed hospital. 1939 and 1940	129,080.40	
City of Plainwell, Allegan County, Michigan		
Toward the construction and equipment of an addition to hospital building and modernization of hospital building. 1940	40,000.00	
City of South Haven, Van Buren County, Mich.		
For laboratory equipment. 1940	115.00	
Total Hospital Grants.	$398,268.70	
TOTAL MICHIGAN COMMUNITY HEALTH PROJECT GRANTS		$1,218,071.98

Exhibit III (Continued)

GRANTS (Continued)

Battle Creek

Ann J. Kellogg School, Battle Creek, Calhoun County, Michigan		
Toward the construction and equipment of an addition to school building. 1938 and 1939 . .	$ 122,181.01	
Battle Creek Camp Fire Girls, Inc.		
Toward the construction and equipment of Camp Kitanniwa. 1937	49,911.77	
Board of Education		
Toward the construction and equipping of two swimming pools located in Southwestern and Southeastern Junior High School Buildings. 1937	36,368.84	
City of Battle Creek, Calhoun County, Michigan		
For land to be used as a public playground. 1936	1,500.00	
For equipment for Barnes Park Playground. 1937	1,650.00	
W. K. Kellogg Junior High School and Auditorium, Battle Creek, Calhoun County, Michigan		
Toward the construction and equipment of Junior High School and Auditorium. 1931–1935, inclusive	607,163.25	
Total Battle Creek Grants		818,774.87
Miscellaneous Grants		
Consultant service, the publication of educational materials and reports, special lectures and miscellaneous grants to various universities, health organizations and medical societies, all for the purpose of promoting child health		42,314.18
Total Grants		$2,760,717.62

MICHIGAN COMMUNITY HEALTH PROJECT	EXHIBIT III (Continued)	
Toward operation of county health departments, provision of certain supplementary health services and educational programs (See detail for year 1940–41 —Exhibit E)		
Allegan County	$ 491,338.57	
Barry County	354,374.91	
Branch County	262,111.69	
Calhoun County	453,958.15	
Eaton County	376,016.01	
Hillsdale County	317,000.61	
Van Buren County	332,804.09	
TOTAL	$2,587,604.03	
Consultant services to communities	$ 260,692.13	
Library services to communities	63,409.42	
Miscellaneous supplies, equipment and publications	59,965.22	
TOTAL MICHIGAN COMMUNITY HEALTH PROJECT		$2,971,670.80
FELLOWSHIP PROGRAM		
Camps	$ 482.99	
Dentistry	9,075.96	
Hospitals	4,111.34	
In-Service training	4,945.43	
Public Health Administration	51,787.93	
Public Health Engineering	95,044.05	
Public Health Nursing	80,564.40	
Schools	2,100.00	
TOTAL FELLOWSHIP PROGRAM		248,112.10
CAMP PROGRAM—CLEAR LAKE, PINE LAKE AND ST. MARY'S LAKE		
Construction	$ 444,633.11	
Operation	627,987.98	
TOTAL CAMP PROGRAM		1,072,621.09
BATTLE CREEK		
Schools		
For special teachers for handicapped children at the Ann J. Kellogg School, maintenance of W. K. Kellogg Auditorium, and Southeastern and Southwestern swimming pools	$ 140,653.44	
Hospital Equipment	13,155.95	
Recreation—Youth Building		
Construction	27,698.29	
Operation	82,734.91	
Direct relief	67,164.30	
TOTAL BATTLE CREEK		331,406.89
TOTAL EXPENDITURES (EXHIBIT II)		$8,228,018.95

Exhibit A

W. K. KELLOGG FOUNDATION

AND

W. K. KELLOGG FOUNDATION TRUST

COMBINED BALANCE SHEET—AUGUST 31, 1941

ASSETS

GENERAL FUND:			
Cash in Banks and on Hand			
Cash balance W. K. Kellogg Foundation (Exhibit C)		$ 911,876.63	
Cash held by W. K. Kellogg Foundation Trust .		35,398.15	$ 947,274.78
Securities, at estimated values as at dates of receipt from donors or at cost to the Foundation, less amortization of premiums (Exhibit F)			11,553,243.94
Other Assets			
Accounts receivable		$ 5,329.12	
Notes receivable (at face amounts)—			
Atlas Properties, Incorporated .	$ 663,798.00		
Others	151,200.00	814,998.00	
Mortgages receivable (at face amounts)		303,968.95	
Life insurance policies		135,708.32	
Claim against closed bank		76,493.15	
Real estate and equipment (at values set up at date of receipt from donors or at cost to the Foundation, less accumulated depreciation from date of acquisition)		767,151.43	2,103,648.97
Total General Fund			$14,604,167.69
W. K. KELLOGG FOUNDATION TRUST FUND			
1,105,000 shares of common stock of Kellogg Company (stated at estimated value as at the several dates of receipt from Founder)			31,970,000.00
			$46,574,167.69

LIABILITIES

GENERAL FUND:	
Amounts provided for 1941–42 expenditures (including $30,000 provided in prior year)	$2,861,790.00
Amounts provided for expenditures to be made subsequent to August 31, 1942	16,875.00
Together	$2,878,665.00
General Fund Balance August 31, 1941 (Exhibit B)	11,725,502.69
Together	$14,604,167.69
W. K. KELLOGG FOUNDATION TRUST FUND	31,970,000.00
	$46,574,167.69

Exhibit B

W. K. KELLOGG FOUNDATION

GENERAL FUND

Balance as at August 31, 1940			$11,663,210.65
Add:			
Gifts—			
Founder	$ 3,398.78		
Others	8,206.68	$ 11,605.46	
Income—			
W. K. Kellogg Foundation Trust	$1,890,267.05		
Dividends on stocks owned	197,943.25		
Dividends on insurance policies	236.50		
Interest received—			
On bonds $ 213,597.69			
Other securities 15,650.52	229,248.21		
Rental income from properties	7,032.50	2,324,727.51	
Profit realized on sale, redemption and exchange of bonds (net) (Exhibit G)		41,326.36	
Liquidating dividends on securities carried at no value		156.00	
Unexpended balance of amounts provided for 1940–41 expenditures		319,282.08	
Refund of portion of amounts advanced in prior years to pay Federal income taxes assessed in respect of income paid W. K. Kellogg Foundation from certain trusts		208,340.19	
Refund of Federal excise taxes paid in a prior year		86,373.64	
Reserve provided in a prior year, no longer required		15,000.00	3,006,811.24
Together			$14,670,021.89
Deduct:			
Amounts provided for 1941–42 expenditures. . .		$2,831,790.00	
Amounts provided for expenditures to be made subsequent to August 31, 1942		11,075.00	
Amortization of bond premiums		55,745.24	
Provision for depreciation of real estate and equipment		41,056.96	
Loss on sale of stock (Exhibit G)		4,718.00	
Loss on sale of office equipment		134.00	2,944,519.20
Balance as at August 31, 1941			$11,725,502.69

Exhibit C

W. K. KELLOGG FOUNDATION

STATEMENT OF RECEIPTS AND DISBURSEMENTS FOR THE YEAR ENDED AUGUST 31, 1941

			Amount
Cash in banks and on hand as at August 31, 1940 (Exhibit II)			$ 915,093.94
RECEIPTS			
Income			
W. K. Kellogg Foundation Trust	$1,890,267.05		
Less—Increase in amount withheld by Corporate Trustee	9,804.10	$1,880,462.95	
Dividends on stocks owned		197,943.25	
Dividends on insurance policies		236.50	
Interest received—			
On bonds	$ 213,597.69		
On other securities	15,650.52	229,248.21	
Rental income from properties		7,032.50	
Total Income		$2,314,923.41	
Gifts			
Founder	$ 2,727.50		
Others	8,206.68	10,934.18	
Other			
Proceeds from securities sold, matured or redeemed	$2,840,727.07		
Collections on notes and mortgages	33,235.28		
Refund of portion of amounts advanced in prior years to pay Federal income taxes assessed in respect of income paid W. K. Kellogg Foundation from certain trusts	208,340.19		
Refund of Federal excise taxes paid in a prior year	86,373.64		
Miscellaneous receipts	235.00	3,168,911.18	5,494,768.77
Together			$6,409,862.71
DEDUCT-DISBURSEMENTS:			
Expenditures (Exhibit D)		$2,303,461.13	
Purchase of investments		3,160,159.12	
Operation of certain properties		32,961.71	
Miscellaneous disbursements		1,404.12	5,497,986.08
Cash in banks and on hand as at August 31, 1941 (Exhibit A)			$ 911,876.63

Exhibit D

W. K. KELLOGG FOUNDATION

STATEMENT OF EXPENDITURES

FOR THE YEAR ENDED AUGUST 31, 1941

ADMINISTRATION AND GENERAL

Administration		
Salaries	$ 37,704.65	
Travel	3,747.35	
Honoraria to Trustees	910.00	
Rent and light	8,906.28	
Legal services and expenses	11,062.21	
Telephone and telegraph	4,879.04	
Auditing	4,750.00	
Insurance—general	1,793.64	
Office furniture and equipment	2,746.87	
Postage and express	1,210.04	
Stationery and office supplies	2,776.89	
Documentary stamps and transfer tax	35.84	
Miscellaneous	5,231.88	
Total	$ 85,754.69	
General		
Investment counsel and safekeeping of securities	16,690.14	
Insurance		
Group life	2,963.02*	
Retirement income (for the years ending August 31, 1940 and August 31, 1941)	53,309.88*	
Study leave	7,801.57*	
Health service	4,401.06*	
Total	$ 85,165.67	
Total Administration and General		$ 170,920.36

*These items include payments for the staffs of the central office, the consultants, the county health departments of the Michigan Community Health Project, and Clear, Pine and St. Mary's Lake Camps.

Exhibit D (Continued)

GRANTS

International		
American Public Health Association		
To conduct an annual rural health conservation contest for all full-time county and district health departments in the United States and Canada	$ 15,000.00	
Harvard University		
Medical School		
For the study and control of communicable diseases of children under war-time conditions in the British Isles	25,000.00	
World Federation of Education Associations		
For a secretariat to facilitate international exchange of health education materials	5,000.00	
Total International Grants		$ 45,000.00
National		
American Foundation for the Blind, Inc.		
For the development of talking books for blind children	$ 13,000.00	
American Public Health Association		
For epidemiological studies concerning the control of communicable diseases	8,278.41	
Columbia University		
College of Physicians and Surgeons		
For research on the causes, the methods of prevention and treatment of rheumatic fever in children	10,000.00	
National Society for the Prevention of Blindness		
For the prevention of blindness and the conservation of vision	200.00	
Total National Grants		31,478.41
State		
Michigan State Department of Health		
Bureau of Laboratories		
For special laboratory equipment for virus research	$ 7,000.00	
Bureau of Maternal Hygiene		
For consultant service in obstetrics for practicing physicians	5,000.00	
Bureau of Public Health Nursing		
For consultant service in nutrition	4,300.00	

GRANTS (Continued)

State (Continued)

Michigan State Nurses Association		
For postgraduate education of registered nurses for replacement service during the emergency	$ 7,800.00	
University of Michigan		
School of Dentistry		
For the enlargement of the faculty to provide graduate and postgraduate courses for practicing dentists	20,000.00	
For the publication of a bulletin regarding graduate and postgraduate courses in dentistry	1,000.00	
School of Medicine		
For field research on the anemias of pregnancy	8,700.00	
For the enlargement of the teaching and research facilities of the Department of Pediatrics	100,000.00	
School of Public Health		
Toward the cost of obtaining a site, constructing and equipping a new building for the School of Public Health	250,000.00	
For the enlargement of the teaching facilities of the School of Public Health for the period 1941–1951	250,000.00	
To provide additional facilities for postgraduate and continued education in the field of public health	25,000.00	
University of Michigan and the Michigan Joint Committee on Health Education		
For public education in health and hygiene	2,000.00	
Total State Grants		$ 680,800.00

Michigan Community Health Project

Schools

Delton W. K. Kellogg Agricultural School, Delton, Barry County, Michigan		
Toward the construction and equipment of an addition to consolidated rural agricultural school building	$ 75,000.00	
Local School Boards in Allegan, Branch, Eaton and Van Buren Counties, Michigan		
For assistance in modernizing rural and village schools	173,621.41	

Exhibit D (Continued)

GRANTS (Continued)

Michigan Community Health Project (Continued)

Schools (Continued)

Wayland Union School, Wayland, Allegan County, Michigan		
Toward the construction and equipment of a consolidated rural agricultural school building.	$ 100,000.00	
Total School Grants	$ 348,621.41	
Hospitals		
City of Albion, Calhoun County, Michigan		
For equipment and remodeling of x-ray department	$ 8,145.00	
City of Allegan, Allegan County, Michigan		
Final payment toward the construction and equipment of a forty-bed hospital building . .	7,248.14	
City of Plainwell, Allegan County, Michigan		
Toward the construction and equipment of a fifteen-bed addition and modernization of the hospital building	20,672.43	
City of South Haven, Van Buren County, Michigan		
Toward the construction and equipment of a forty-bed hospital building	155,228.32	
Community Health Center of Branch County, Coldwater, Michigan		
For an electrocardiograph	699.57	
Hillsdale Community Health Center, Hillsdale, Hillsdale County, Michigan		
For diagnostic equipment	119.00	
Total Hospital Grants	$ 192,112.46	
Starr Commonwealth for Boys		
For pasteurizing and bottling equipment and installation	$ 3,500.00	
Total Michigan Community Health Project Grants		$ 544,233.87
Battle Creek		
Leila Y. Post Montgomery Hospital, Battle Creek, Calhoun County, Michigan		
For a projector, a Sweet's Eye Localizer and a Mueller Giant Eye Magnet	$ 1,506.25	
Battle Creek Camp Fire Girls, Inc.		
For the improvement of water supply at Camp Kitanniwa	800.00	
Total Battle Creek Grants		2,306.25
Miscellaneous Grants.		926.54
Total Grants		$1,304,745.07

EXHIBIT D (Continued)

MICHIGAN COMMUNITY HEALTH PROJECT		
Toward operation of county health departments, provision of certain supplementary health services and educational programs (see Exhibit E)		
Allegan County	$ 81,161.51	
Barry County	59,517.90	
Branch County	71,069.40	
Calhoun County	90,379.00	
Eaton County	68,219.64	
Hillsdale County	59,182.87	
Van Buren County	59,825.72	
TOTAL	$ 489,356.04	
Consultant services to communities	84,942.59	
Library services to communities	9,682.38	
Miscellaneous supplies, equipment and publications	9,294.37	
TOTAL MICHIGAN COMMUNITY HEALTH PROJECT		$ 593,275.38
FELLOWSHIP PROGRAM		
Camps	$ 2,374.53	
Dentistry	5,370.66	
Hospitals	175.61	
Medicine	1,224.25	
Public Health Administration	2,536.80	
Public Health Engineering	19,799.29	
Public Health Nursing	20,903.47	
Schools	3,760.14	
TOTAL FELLOWSHIP PROGRAM		56,144.75
CAMP PROGRAM—CLEAR LAKE, PINE LAKE AND ST. MARY'S LAKE		
Construction	$ 6,608.63	
Operation	136,369.78	
TOTAL CAMP PROGRAM		142,978.41
BATTLE CREEK		
Schools		
For special teachers for handicapped children at the Ann J. Kellogg School; maintenance of W. K. Kellogg Auditorium, and Southeastern and Southwestern Swimming Pools	$ 16,357.68	
Recreation—Youth Building		
Construction	7,690.47	
Operation	8,649.01	
Direct relief	2,700.00	
TOTAL BATTLE CREEK		35,397.16
TOTAL EXPENDITURES (EXHIBIT C)		$2,303,461.13

Exhibit E

W. K. KELLOGG FOUNDATION

MICHIGAN COMMUNITY HEALTH PROJECT

DETAILED STATEMENT OF EXPENDITURES

SEPTEMBER 1, 1940 THROUGH AUGUST 31, 1941

	ALLEGAN	BARRY	BRANCH	CALHOUN	EATON	HILLSDALE	VAN BUREN	TOTAL
Health Department*	$20,363.98	$18,180.16	$14,900.09	$25,218.99	$22,301.33	$16,072.58	$18,000.00	$135,037.13
Service								
Medical	$ 7,362.04	$ 3,052.25	$ 3,741.00	$ 7,418.13	$ 3,317.00	$ 3,808.50	$ 4,826.50	$ 33,525.42
Dental	8,182.50	3,401.25	16,469.75	13,146.00	8,622.50	5,475.30	3,834.00	59,131.30
Hospital	8,712.93	2,869.91	4,901.25	7,419.77	2,426.14	4,505.57	5,739.33	36,574.90
Total Service	$24,257.47	$ 9,323.41	$25,112.00	$27,983.90	$14,365.64	$13,789.37	$14,399.83	$129,231.62
Education								
Physicians	$ 1,540.08	$ 1,275.08	$ 1,500.08	$ 1,189.83	$ 1,700.36	$ 1,233.82	$ 2,021.07	$ 10,460.32
Dentists	765.00	436.00	380.00	1,670.00	815.00	60.00	565.92	4,691.92
Nurses	717.00	412.00	128.00	248.20	58.00	475.85	84.60	2,123.65
Teachers	5,524.24	5,985.69	3,976.34	7,496.23	6,958.45	5,522.61	3,892.78	39,356.34
Special Groups	6,973.65	3,542.58	6,876.88	7,699.69	8,632.38	5,676.13	5,272.89	44,674.20
Total Education	$15,519.97	$11,651.35	$12,861.30	$18,303.95	$18,164.19	$12,968.41	$11,837.26	$101,306.43
Welfare								
Youth Organizations	$ 1,500.00	$ 880.00	$ 525.00	$ 1,878.00	$ 1,805.00	$ 1,645.00	$ 588.00	$ 8,821.00
Relief	1,801.12	1,339.00	1,076.78	2,286.26	2,167.44	2,667.48	2,216.00	13,554.08
Total Welfare	$ 3,301.12	$ 2,219.00	$ 1,601.78	$ 4,164.26	$ 3,972.44	$ 4,312.48	$ 2,804.00	$ 22,375.08
Local Libraries	$17,718.97	$18,143.98	$16,594.23	$14,707.90	$ 9,416.04	$12,040.03	$12,784.63	$101,405.78
County Totals	$81,161.51	$59,517.90	$71,069.40	$90,379.00	$68,219.64	$59,182.87	$59,825.72	$489,356.04

*Paid to County Boards of Supervisors toward cost of operating health departments.

EXHIBIT F

W. K. KELLOGG FOUNDATION

STATEMENT OF SECURITIES AS AT AUGUST 31, 1941

BONDS

U. S. Government	Face Amount	Ledger Value[1]	Market Value
Treasury Bonds			
3¼s due 10-15-45/43	$ 50,000	$ 51,354.59	$ 53,218.75
2½s due 12-15-45	400,000	413,950.72	432,375.00
3⅜s due 6-15-47/43	50,000	51,730.96	52,937.50
3¼s due 4-15-46/44	500,000	536,738.21	537,500.00
2¾s due 9-15-47/45	250,000	254,866.28	271,015.63
3s due 6-15-48/46	100,000	106,586.61	110,312.50
2½s due 9-15-48	400,000	428,246.80	435,875.00
3⅛s due 6-15-49/46	290,000	316,976.16	321,628.12
2s due 3-15-50/48	490,000	501,254.69	507,609.38
2¾s due 3-15-51/48	250,000	265,255.51	273,593.75
2½s due 9-15-52/50	250,000	260,781.25	270,078.13
2¼s due 12-15-53/51	80,000	83,269.28	85,300.00
2¾s due 6-15-54/51	150,000	157,788.56	165,046.88
2½s due 3-15-54/52	150,000	152,543.75	158,578.12
Savings Bonds			
Series G			
2½s due 5-1-53	50,000	50,000.00	49,400.00
Series D			
Due 8-1-49	7,500	7,500.00	7,800.00
Due 1-1-50	7,500	7,500.00	7,700.00
Treasury Notes			
1¾s due 3-15-42	250,000	250,756.58	255,312.50
2s due 9-15-42	250,000	252,824.20	258,125.00
1⅛s due 12-15-43	100,000	102,359.38	102,312.50
¾s due 9-15-44	300,000	299,825.00	301,593.75
Federal Farm Mortgage Corp.			
3s due 5-15-49/44	200,000	205,548.46	213,437.50
Home Owners Loan Corp.			
2¼s due 7-1-44/42	200,000	201,024.16	203,812.50
1½s due 6-1-47/45	200,000	202,765.38	205,687.50
3s due 5-1-52/44	50	50.00	53.31
Reconstruction Finance Corp.			
1s due 4-15-44	70,000	70,000.00	70,503.13
Municipal			
Ann Arbor, Mich., W/W Imp.			
3¾s due 6-1-58	4,000	3,326.13	5,097.20
Audubon County, Iowa, Prim. Road Ref.			
1¾s due 5-1-43	50,000	50,000.00	51,035.00
Battle Creek, Mich., Sewer Improvement Rev.			
4s due 7-1-51	2,000	2,074.42	2,240.00
4s due 7-1-52	3,000	3,121.05	3,394.80

EXHIBIT F (Continued)

BONDS (Continued)

Municipal (*Continued*)	*Face Amount*	*Ledger Value*[1]	*Market Value*
Champaign County, Ill., Ref.			
5s due 11-1-44	$ 25,000	$ 26,344.24	$ 28,277.50
5s due 11-1-45	25,000	26,765.12	29,225.00
City of Chicago, General			
4s due 1-1-42	55,000	55,511.88	55,621.50
Chicago Park District			
Refunding E			
3½s due 5-1-56/46	20,000	20,467.10	21,958.00
Refunding B			
4s due 9-1-55/3-1-46	50,000	53,997.36	55,805.00
Chicago Sanitary District, Ref. B			
4¼s due 1-1-55/43	25,000	26,268.58	26,050.00
4s due 1-1-55/43	50,000	53,014.20	51,935.00
4¼s due 1-1-55/46	10,000	11,009.12	11,222.00
4¼s due 1-1-55/48	45,000	51,288.03	51,525.00
Guthrie County, Iowa, Prim. Road Ref.			
1¾s due 5-1-42	20,000	20,047.56	20,182.00
1¾s due 5-1-45	30,000	29,649.42	31,044.00
State of Illinois			
Relief			
3¼s due 12-15-43	25,000	25,324.99	25,952.50
4½s due 12-15-43	25,000	26,578.18	27,302.50
Highway			
4s due 5-1-47	15,000	16,521.00	17,469.00
Kansas City, Kansas, Gen'l Imp.			
4¾s due 11-1-43	40,000	42,844.65	43,600.00
Kansas City, Missouri, S/D			
4½s due 1-1-43	50,000	51,736.94	52,505.00
Marion County, Iowa, Prim. Road Ref.			
1¾s due 5-1-45	40,000	39,532.56	41,392.00
Miami Conservancy District, Ohio			
5½s due 12-1-43	25,000	26,807.95	27,607.50
State of Michigan			
Hwy. Imp.			
5½s due 9-15-41	100,000	101,551.74	100,000.00
Soldiers Bonus			
5½s due 10-15-41	15,000	15,187.60	15,084.00
New York Loan for Emergency Unemployment Relief			
2¼s due 9-25-43	50,000	50,171.00	51,900.00
Polk County, Iowa, Fd.			
2¼s due 11-1-42	25,000	25,124.77	25,550.00
San Bernardino H/S Dist., Calif.			
2¼s due 1-1-42	25,000	25,051.31	25,125.00
Sedgwick County, Kansas, Relief			
2s due 11-1-44	20,000	20,176.54	20,810.00
2s due 11-1-45	20,000	20,142.74	21,008.00
2s due 11-1-46	20,000	20,123.31	21,112.00

Exhibit F (Continued)

BONDS (Continued)

Municipal (Continued)	*Face Amount*	*Ledger Value*[1]	*Market Value*
Wichita, Kansas, Int. Imp. Ref.			
2s due 2-1-42	$ 15,000	$ 15,038.86	$ 15,157.50
3s due 2-1-43	15,000	15,100.63	15,523.50
3s due 2-1-44	10,000	10,110.55	10,537.00
Public Utility			
American Tel. & Tel. Co.			
5½s due 11-1-43	50,000	52,194.92	50,400.00
Columbia Gas & Elec. Corp.			
5s due 5-1-52	15,000	15,036.75	15,562.50
Consolidated Edison Co. of N. Y.			
3¼s due 4-1-46	50,000	50,937.50	52,250.00
Detroit Edison Company			
4s due 10-1-65	5,000	5,145.40	5,575.00
Oklahoma Gas & Elec. Co.			
4s due 12-1-46	47,000	47,877.80	48,410.00
Pacific Gas & Elec. Co.			
6s due 12-1-41	25,000	25,468.33	25,330.00
Peoples Gas Light & Coke Co.			
5s due 9-1-47	100,000	111,220.48	115,875.00
St. Paul Gas Light Co.			
5s due 3-1-44	75,000	79,512.21	82,395.00
Wisconsin Power & Light Co.			
4s due 6-1-66	25,000	23,406.25	26,000.00
Real Estate			
Michigan State Development Co. of Battle Creek, Michigan			
6s due 6-1-45	1,000	1,000.00	600.00
S-H Realty Co.			
6s due 3-1-45	30,000	30,000.00[3]	15,000.00
Foreign			
Bell Telephone Co. of Canada			
5s due 6-1-57	15,000	15,083.00	16,706.25
Dominion of Canada			
2¼s due 1-15-44/43	50,000	49,437.50	48,875.00
2½s due 8-15-45/43	50,000	50,361.04	48,250.00
4s due 10-1-60/50	100,000	109,655.62	100,875.00
Railroad			
Bessemer & Lake Erie R. R. Co., Equip.			
2¼s due 3-1-42	50,000	50,117.92	50,400.00
Canadian Pacific Ry., Equip.			
5s due 7-1-44	50,000	52,710.86	52,250.00
Chesapeake & Ohio Ry. Co., Equip. Trust			
2s due 3-1-42	50,000	50,023.68	50,350.00
3s due 10-1-46	25,000	26,097.14	26,987.50
3s due 10-1-47	25,000	26,136.20	27,032.50

Exhibit F (Continued)

BONDS (Continued)

Railroad (Continued)	Face Amount	Ledger Value[1]	Market Value
Clinchfield Railroad Co., Equip. 2¼s due 3-1-42	$ 50,000	$ 50,117.80	$ 50,400.00
Great Northern Ry., Equip. 2s due 3-1-42	50,000	49,999.98	50,330.00
Missouri Pacific Railroad Co., Ref. Mtge. 5s due 3-1-77	15,000	15,025.94[3]	4,162.50
New York, New Haven & Hartford R. R. Co., Equip. 4½s due 3-15-43	10,000	9,861.97	10,543.00
Reading Company, Equip. 4½s due 11-1-44	50,000	53,990.56	55,200.00
Southern Pacific Railroad Co., Equip. 2¼s due 11-1-43	20,000	20,097.05	20,600.00
St. Louis-San Francisco Ry. Co., Cons. Mtge. 4½s due 3-1-78	15,000	13,738.80[3]	2,325.00
Totals, Bonds	$7,042,050	$7,295,760.76	$7,405,738.20

[1]Ledger values represent estimated values as at dates of receipt from donors or cost to the Foundation, less amortization of premiums.
[2]Nominal value.
[3]Interest in default.

Exhibit F (Continued)

COMMON STOCKS	*Number of Shares*	*Ledger Value*[1]	*Market Value*
Air Reduction Company	2,000	$ 99,973.16	$ 85,750.00
American Brake Shoe & Foundry Co.	1,500	53,679.36	52,125.00
American Can Company	800	99,329.34	66,000.00
American Tobacco Company, "B"	800	75,375.96	56,200.00
Atlas Properties, Inc.	500	5,000.00	1.00[2]
Chemical Bank & Trust Company	1,000	44,119.72	45,125.00
Commonwealth Edison Company	2,000	60,933.75	51,500.00
Commonwealth & Southern Corp.	512	2,496.00	224.00
Continental Can Company, Inc.	1,500	98,524.86	55,125.00
Country Club Land Company	25	25.00	1.00[2]
Curtiss-Wright Corp.	91	312.00	875.88
Dow Chemical Company	400	58,249.51	52,500.00
E. I. DuPont deNemours & Co.	700	94,339.70	109,112.50
Eastman Kodak Company	700	106,542.50	98,875.00
Eaton Manufacturing Company	1,131	15,551.25	37,323.00
General Electric Company	3,000	102,251.03	98,250.00
General Motors Corporation	2,000	95,500.33	78,500.00
W. T. Grant Company	1,400	42,973.02	46,900.00
Guaranty Trust Co. of New York	200	54,394.68	57,200.00
Gull Lake Association	55	550.00	1.00[2]
Hazel-Atlas Glass Company	1,000	109,846.75	91,000.00
Humble Oil & Refining Company	1,800	120,891.91	115,650.00
International Business Machines Corp.	735	104,936.80	116,130.00
International Shoe Company	500	17,393.55	14,375.00
Kellogg Company	45,225	1,304,247.50	938,418.75
Liggett & Myers Tobacco Co., "B"	500	46,072.31	42,500.00
Monsanto Chemical Company	1,000	91,134.71	91,750.00
National Lead Company	5,000	96,585.00	91,875.00
National Steel Corporation	1,000	71,319.89	53,750.00
Old-Merchants Nat'l Bank & Trust Company	3,188	1.00	1.00[2]
Old Securities Company	520	6,341.00	4,160.00
Parke, Davis & Company	2,000	89,314.51	58,500.00
J. C. Penney Company	1,000	79,533.23	87,500.00
Peerless Cement Corp.	450	45.00	2,925.00
Pittsburgh Plate Glass Company	1,000	94,750.48	81,000.00
Procter & Gamble Company	2,000	107,467.68	119,500.00
R. J. Reynolds Tobacco Co., "B"	1,500	84,312.50	48,375.00
Standard Oil Company of California	3,000	90,039.43	69,750.00
Standard Oil Company of Indiana	3,000	84,881.88	97,875.00
Standard Oil Company of New Jersey	1,500	65,792.63	65,250.00
Texas Corporation	1,500	67,914.69	64,125.00
Union Carbide & Carbon Corp.	1,400	96,014.18	110,250.00
Union Steam Pump Company	1,800	36,000.00	36,000.00
United Fruit Company	1,000	79,357.07	71,750.00
United Shoe Machinery Co.	1,000	58,386.51	61,000.00
United States Gypsum Company	1,000	84,081.80	58,500.00
F. W. Woolworth Company	1,000	60,700.00	30,000.00
TOTALS, COMMON STOCKS		$ 4,257,483.18	$ 3,613,498.13
TOTALS, BONDS AND STOCKS		$11,553,243.94	$11,019,236.33

Exhibit G W. K. KELLOGG FOUNDATION

SECURITIES PURCHASED, EXCHANGED, SOLD OR REDEEMED DURING YEAR ENDED AUGUST 31, 1941

PURCHASED

BONDS	Face Amount	Cost
U. S. Government		
Treasury Bonds		
2½s due 3-15-58/56	$ 100,000	$ 103,078.13[1]
2s due 12-15-50/48	490,000	514,498.44
2½s due 12-15-45	150,000	162,046.88
3¼s due 4-15-46/44	100,000	109,656.25
2½s due 9-15-48	300,000	327,671.88
3⅛s due 6-15-49/46	140,000	157,609.38
2s due 3-15-50/48	490,000	501,254.69
2¼s due 12-15-53/51	80,000	83,425.00
2½s due 3-15-54/52	100,000	102,312.50[1]
2½s due 3-15-54/52	50,000	50,231.25
Savings Bonds		
2½s due 5-1-53	50,000	50,000.00
Treasury Notes		
1⅛s due 12-15-43/41	100,000	102,359.38
¾s due 9-15-44	300,000	299,825.00
Reconstruction Finance Corp.		
1s due 4-15-44	70,000	70,000.00
Industrial		
Crane Company		
2¼s due 10-1-50	50,000	50,750.00
Public Utility		
People's Gas Light & Coke Co.		
5s due 9-1-47	5,000	5,861.39
TOTALS	$2,575,000	$2,690,580.17

COMMON STOCKS	Number of Shares	Cost
Air Reduction Company, Inc.	500	$ 21,035.66
American Brake Shoe & Foundry Co.	600	22,234.16
American Can Company	200	17,017.56
American Tobacco Company, "B"	200	13,775.96
Chemical Bank & Trust Co. of New York	1,000	44,119.72
Continental Can Co., Inc.	500	18,555.75
Dow Chemical Company	200	27,243.30
General Electric Company	3,000	102,251.03
W. T. Grant Company	700	21,837.68
Guaranty Trust Co. of New York	200	54,394.68
Humble Oil & Refining Company	300	17,854.63
International Business Machines Corp.	175	27,153.88
Liggett & Myers Tobacco Company, "B"	500	46,072.31
National Steel Corp.	600	40,614.89
Standard Oil Co. of California	1,000	22,776.93
Standard Oil Co. of Indiana	2,000	55,917.27
Standard Oil Co. of New Jersey	458	16,737.15
Texas Corporation	500	19,693.53
Union Carbide & Carbon Corp.	400	27,276.68
United Shoe Machinery Corp.	1,000	58,386.51
TOTAL		$674,949.28

REDEEMED
BONDS

	Face Amount or Number of Shares	Ledger Value[2]	Amount Received
Industrial			
Crane Company			
3½s due 6–1–51	$ 50,000	$ 50,721.77	$ 50,500.00
Municipal			
Benton Harbor, Michigan, Ref.			
4s due 3–1–45/40	3,000	3,014.80	3,000.00
Chautauqua County, New York, Hwy.			
5s due 4–1–41	25,000	25,000.00	25,000.00
Guthrie County, Iowa			
Prim. Road Ref.			
1¾s due 5–1–41	25,000	25,000.00	25,000.00
State of Illinois, Hwy.			
4s due 5–1–41	25,000	25,000.00	25,000.00
State of Michigan			
Soldiers Bonus			
5¾s due 7–15–41	10,000	10,000.00	10,000.00
Sussex County, Delaware			
Hwy. Imp.			
3s due 9–1–40	25,000	25,000.00	25,000.00
Public Utility			
Appalachian Electric Co.			
4s due 2–1–63	50,000	49,375.00	53,000.00
Georgia Power Company			
5s due 3–1–67	1,000	825.72	1,041.67
Oklahoma Gas & Electric Co.			
4s due 12–1–46	3,000	3,061.32	3,075.00
Public Service Co. of Oklahoma			
4s due 2–1–66	25,000	25,000.00	26,000.00
Railroad			
Great Northern Railway			
Equip. Trust of 1937			
2s due 3–1–41	25,000	25,000.00	25,000.00
Pennsylvania Railroad			
Equip. Trust			
2¾s due 12–1–40	65,000	65,000.00	65,000.00
Southern Pacific Co.			
Equip. Trust of 1936			
2¼s due 11–1–40	35,000	35,000.00	35,000.00
Real Estate			
Old-Merchants Nat'l Bank			
& Trust Co., Trustee			
5½s due 2–1–35	4,500	4,463.08	3,637.50

Exhibit G (Continued)

SOLD

BONDS

U. S. Government	Face Amount or Number of Shares	Ledger Value[2]	Amount Received
Treasury			
3¼s due 8-1-41	$ 100,000	$ 100,684.24	$ 103,078.13[1]
3¼s due 8-1-41	300,000	302,052.74	308,390.63
3⅜s due 3-15-43/41	400,000	410,777.60	405,000.00
3⅜s due 6-15-47/43	200,000	210,157.57	216,562.50
2s due 12-15-50/48	490,000	513,057.28	517,256.25
2½s due 3-15-58/56	100,000	103,078.13	104,593.75
3¼s due 10-15-45/43	350,000	360,536.39	380,117.19
Treasury Notes			
1⅜s due 6-15-41	100,000	100,019.53	102,312.50[1]
¾s due 3-15-45	200,000	201,687.00	201,765.63
Federal Farm Mtge. Corp.			
2¾s due 3-1-47/42	200,000	203,808.90	207,000.00
Industrial			
Crane Company			
2¼s due 10-1-50	50,000	50,732.75	50,040.00
Municipal			
Cook County, Illinois			
Ref., Ser. B			
4s due 1-1-51/46	5,000	5,495.80	5,536.45
Des Moines, Iowa, H/S Bldg.			
4½s due 5-1-42	40,000	41,428.12	42,670.00
Public Utility			
The Western Union Telegraph Co.			
5s due 3-1-60	15,000	15,235.60	11,962.50
Totals	$2,921,500	$2,990,213.34	$3,031,539.70
Profit		41,326.36	—
		$3,031,539.70	$3,031,539.70

COMMON STOCKS

United States Tobacco Co.	500	$17,555.00	$12,837.00
Loss		—	4,718.00
		$17,555.00	$17,555.00

LIQUIDATING DIVIDENDS RECEIVED

Old Securities Company	
$5 per share on 317 shares	$1,585.00

SUMMARY

Ledger value of securities, August 31, 1940		$11,252,813.07
Bonds purchased		2,690,580.17
Stocks purchased		674,949.28
Together		$14,618,342.52
Deduct		
Ledger value of securities sold, exchanged or redeemed		
Bonds	$2,990,213.34	
Stocks	17,555.00	
Liquidating dividends	1,585.00	
Amortization of bond premiums for year ended August 31, 1941	55,745.24	3,065,098.58
Ledger Value of Securities, August 31, 1941		$11,553,243.94[2]

[1]Exchanged.

[2]Ledger values represent estimated values as at dates of receipt from donors or cost to the Foundation, less amortization of premiums.

APPENDIX

APPENDIX A

W. K. KELLOGG FOUNDATION TRUST

THE W. K. Kellogg Foundation Trust exists under an agreement dated July 27, 1934, as amended and interpreted by an instrument dated July 13, 1935. Glenn A. Cross, George B. Darling and Emory W. Morris are the present co-trustees and Harris Trust and Savings Bank is the present corporate trustee of W. K. Kellogg Foundation Trust. W. K. Kellogg is the settlor of the trust.

The trust agreement, as so amended and interpreted, makes the following provisions regarding distribution of income and principal of the trust estate:

ARTICLE THREE

Distribution Provisions

THE trust estate shall be distributed, both as to income and principal, in the following manner:

3.01. The entire net income of the trust estate shall be paid unto said W. K. KELLOGG FOUNDATION—hereinafter sometimes called the "Foundation"—in convenient installments, but not less frequently than quarter-yearly, perpetually or until the trust estate shall be exhausted, to be used by it exclusively for those purposes set forth in its Articles of Association as the same now exist or as the same from time to time may be amended, and which also shall be such purposes as the law deems charitable in the legal sense of that word. If in any calendar year after the year 1934 the net income payable to the Foundation by virtue of the provisions of this paragraph shall be less than the sum of five hundred thousand dollars ($500,000), then, upon the request of the Foundation, the trustees shall withdraw from the corpus of the trust estate such sum or sums as when added to the net income of the trust estate so available for the benefit of the Foundation will permit the trustees to pay to the Foundation in such year the sum of five hundred thousand dollars ($500,000), and the trustees shall make payment of such amount to the Foundation.

3.02. If the Foundation shall desire to purchase real estate for the corporate purposes of the Foundation, or to make expenditures for enlargements of and/or improvements to or on any of its property or properties, or construct, remodel or enlarge buildings from time to time owned by the Foundation, and used in connection with or in aid of the corporate purposes of the Foundation, then the trustees, in their discretion, may pay to the Foundation, at any time and from time to time, such sum or sums out of the corpus of the trust estate as the Foundation may request for any such purpose and as in the opinion of the trustees may be reasonably necessary or desirable for any such purpose, upon such terms and conditions as may be agreed upon between the Foundation and the trustees; provided, however, that during the settlor's lifetime, if he shall be under no legal disability, no amounts shall be paid pursuant to the provisions of this paragraph without the prior approval of the settlor.

3.03. If at any time, in the opinion of a majority of the board of directors of the Foundation, resort should be made to the corpus of the trust estate for additional funds to enable the Foundation to carry out its corporate purposes, the trustees, in their discretion, may pay to the Foundation, out of the corpus of the trust estate, such sum or sums from time to time as the Foundation may request and as the trustees are of opinion shall be reasonably desirable, not to exceed, however, in any one calendar year, two and one-half per cent (2½%) of the corpus of the trust estate as the same shall be valued by the trustees,* or the sum of five hundred thousand dollars ($500,000), whichever is the greater; provided, however, that during the settlor's lifetime, if he shall be under no legal disability, no amounts shall be paid pursuant to the provisions of this paragraph without the prior approval of the settlor. Any payment made under this paragraph shall be in addition to the payments authorized by the foregoing paragraphs hereof.

3.04. The liberal provisions herein contained, authorizing resort to be made to corpus of the trust estate to execute the corporate purposes of the Foundation, are not intended to encourage waste or inefficiency. But it is not intended that the corpus of the trust estate shall be held intact as a perpetual trust. It is the philosophy and purpose of the settlor to make available to the Foundation for the execution of its corporate purposes in an efficient and effective manner the entire trust estate over a period of fifty (50) years, although this statement of intent shall not be construed to be a limitation upon the duration of the trust hereby created. The settlor records his hope that the record of the Foundation during that period of time will be such that if and when the trust estate hereby created shall be exhausted, others will be impressed by the record and work of the Foundation to such an extent that they will be moved to contribute such financial assistance, if any, as may be necessary to enable the Foundation thereafter to continue its work.

*Certain additions being about to be made to the principal of the trust estate, it was provided in the above mentioned agreement of July 13, 1935, as follows:

The phrase in paragraph 3.03 of said agreement reading as follows: "two and one-half per cent (2½%) of the corpus of the trust estate as the same shall be valued by the trustees," shall be interpreted to mean two and one-half per cent (2½%) of the corpus of the trust estate as originally constituted, plus all additions thereto, as the same shall be valued by the trustees at the time any payment is to be made out of corpus to the Foundation. For illustration: Assuming the original corpus of the trust estate to be one hundred X dollars and that additions shall have been made thereto amounting to one hundred X dollars, and that the trustees shall have made distributions of corpus, so that the corpus and the additions thereto shall have been reduced to fifty per cent (50%) thereof, the trustees nevertheless may pay to the Foundation two and one-half per cent (2½%) of two hundred X dollars, assuming there has been no increase or diminution in value of corpus except as a result of distributions. If there has been increase or diminution in value of corpus resulting otherwise than from distributions, the amount which may be paid shall be proportionately increased or reduced.

3.05. The following requirements have been made by W. K. Kellogg, the founder of the Foundation, in respect of its management:

(a) All sums, whether representing corpus or income, received by the Foundation pursuant to the provisions hereof, and notwithstanding any other provision hereof, shall be used by the Foundation to carry out only those purposes set forth in its Articles of Association, as the same now exist, or as the same from time to time may be amended, which are also such purposes as the law deems charitable in the legal sense of that word, and no substantial part of the activities of the Foundation shall be carrying on propaganda, or otherwise attempting, to influence legislation. Said Articles of Association shall never be amended so that any part of the net earnings of the Foundation shall inure to the benefit of any private stockholder or individual.

(b) The Foundation at all times shall function efficiently, and it should maintain a paid secretary and such paid lecturer or lecturers as may be found useful, all at a fair and reasonable compensation; it shall make and at all times maintain and preserve complete records of all of its activities and transactions; and it shall cause an audit of its financial records to be made by a disinterested auditor or firm of auditors approved by the trustees at least once each year.

(c) The directors in attendance at meetings of the board of directors of the Foundation may receive from its corporate funds such compensation as may be fixed by the bylaws of the Foundation or resolutions adopted by its board of directors, and as in the opinion of the trustees shall be reasonable, plus necessary expenses incurred in attending such meetings.

(d) The treasurer of the Foundation at all times shall be bonded in such amount and with such security as shall be specified from time to time by the trustees.

(e) The board of directors shall convene in Battle Creek, Michigan, not less frequently than once each month. The board of directors of the Foundation shall not be permitted to become less than seven (7) in number.

3.06. Notwithstanding the foregoing provisions hereof, if within a period of three (3) months next prior to the making of any corpus or income payment by the trustees to the Foundation hereunder, the board of directors of the Foundation (1) shall have become and remained less than seven (7) in number during the entire period of three (3) months, or (2) shall have failed to meet in Battle Creek, Michigan, at least three (3) times with a quorum present, or (3) shall have failed, after request of the trustees, to have the treasurer of the Foundation bonded in the amount and with the security specified and approved by the trustees, or (4) shall have failed, after request of the trustees, to make and file with the trustees an audit at least annually, or (5) shall have authorized or permitted any funds of the Foundation to be used for any purpose other than one exclusively charitable in the legal sense of that word and one set forth in its Articles of Association as the same now exist or as the same may from time to time be amended, or (6) shall have amended said Articles of Association so that the net earnings of the Foundation shall inure in whole or in part to the benefit of any private stockholder or individual, or (7) if a substantial part of its activities shall be carrying on propaganda, or otherwise attempting, to influence legislation, then the trustees shall withhold such income or corpus payment until they receive assurances that such condition or omission has been or speedily will be remedied. If at any time payments of income and principal hereunder shall have been suspended pursuant to the provisions of this paragraph for a period of six (6) months, then the trustees themselves shall expend, within the State of Michigan, the net income to which the Foundation is entitled pursuant to the provisions hereof, in furtherance of the charitable objects set forth in the Articles of Association of the Foundation as now existing or as the same from time to time may be amended within the limitations aforesaid (but not for the benefit of any private stockholder or individual of the Foundation, nor for carrying on propaganda, or otherwise attempting, to influence legislation) until such time as the board of directors of the Foundation shall have remedied the condition or omission, causing the suspension of payments as aforesaid; provided further that if such condition or omission shall not be remedied within a period of two (2) years from and after the suspension of such payments as aforesaid, or if the Foundation at any time shall be dissolved or otherwise lose its corporate existence, or shall abandon and entirely cease functioning in any manner whatsoever, then the trustees immediately upon the expiration of two (2) years from and after the suspension of such payments as aforesaid, or upon such dissolution, abandonment by the Foundation of its work, or cessation of its activities shall thereafter make all payments to which the Foundation otherwise would be entitled or which could be paid to it by virtue of the provisions hereof for scientific research, and the promotion thereof, within the State of Michigan, for the suppression, prevention, treatment, and cure of diseases of the human body, in such manner as in the opinion of the trustees will most effectively carry out such purposes. The trustees in the making of such payments may avail themselves of and make payments through corporations or organizations, now or hereafter existing, maintaining institutions for any one or more of the charitable purposes aforesaid, or to reputable charitable corporations or organizations undertaking to distribute and apply such funds to any one or more of such purposes; provided that any such organization or corporation to which any payment may be made by the trustees hereunder shall be one, no part of the net earnings of which inure to the benefit of any private stockholder or individual, and no substantial part of the activities of which is carrying on propaganda, or otherwise attempting, to influence legislation. If the limits of the State of Michigan shall be extended beyond their present boundaries, said funds shall be applied within the territory of the State of Michigan as so extended.

3.07. If for the purpose of reducing taxes to which the Foundation, the trustees, or the income or the corpus of the trust estate may be subjected, or for the purpose of more fully effectuating the devotion of the trust estate and the net income thereof to the purposes for which this trust has been created or for the purpose of obtaining relief from other burdens or expenses (except reasonable fees for the services and the expenses of the trustees hereunder) which the Foundation, the trustees, or the trust estate would not be required to pay or be liable for if the Foundation were the owner of the trust estate in its own right, or if for other reasons, at any time in the future it shall become desirable that this trust be terminated and the corpus and undistributed net income thereof be transferred to the Foundation absolutely, it shall be the duty of the trustees so to convey the same, provided:

(a) Five sevenths (5/7) of the total number of the directors of the Foundation then in office and all of the trustees shall join in the execution of an instrument or concurrent instruments stating the fact of such desirability and their determination so to cause the transfer of the trust estate to the Foundation absolutely, or

(b) A court of competent jurisdiction finds it desirable that this trust be terminated and the corpus be so transferred because of any of the reasons hereinbefore stated. Any trustee shall have the right, at the expense of the trust estate, to take any proceeding authorized by law to review any decree or judgment aforesaid.

3.08. If at any time this trust or any part thereof shall be held by a court of competent jurisdiction to be void in such essential particulars that the same shall fail, in whole or in part, then the trust estate or such part thereof as to which this trust shall have been held to be void shall be distributed to and vest in the Foundation absolutely free from all trusts herein expressed.

The above trust agreement may be changed, amended or modified by the W. K. Kellogg Foundation during the settlor's lifetime, with the settlor's written consent. After the settlor's death, or during his lifetime if he shall be under legal disability which has been declared by a court of competent jurisdiction, amendments and modifications may be made by action of a majority of the board of directors (now trustees) of the Foundation, with the consent of all acting trustees of the trust. But Article Three of the trust agreement (above quoted), regarding the beneficiaries of the trust, and the persons, corporations or institutions to which the trustees are authorized or directed to make payments of net income or corpus, cannot be changed, although the time of payment or delivery to them, or any of them, may be accelerated, or it may be provided that the whole or any portion of the corpus or income of the trust estate may be paid at once to the Foundation. By the trust agreement the settlor relinquished the right to revoke, change, amend, or modify the trust agreement or the trust thereby evidenced, in whole or in part, the intention being that the agreement and the trust should be irrevocable, except as provided in the trust agreement.

Appendix B

ARTICLES OF ASSOCIATION OF THE W. K. KELLOGG FOUNDATION

(Including Amendments Through June 27, 1939)

WE, the undersigned, desiring to become incorporated under the provisions of Act. No. 84, of the Public Acts of Michigan for 1921, providing for the "organization, regulation, and classification of domestic corporations," etc., do hereby make, execute and adopt the following articles of association, to wit:

ARTICLE I

The name or title by which said corporation is to be known in law is W. K. Kellogg Foundation.

ARTICLE II

This corporation shall proceed under Section 2, Chapter 1, Part I, of the above named act.

ARTICLE III

The purposes for which this corporation is formed are and forever shall be "benevolent" and "social," within the meaning of those terms as employed in Section 3 of Article XII of the constitution of the State of Michigan now in force, and shall consist of receiving and administering funds for educational or charitable purposes. The purposes of this corporation shall be confined, however, to receiving and administering funds for the promotion of the health, education, and welfare of mankind, but principally of children and youth, directly or indirectly, without regard to sex, race, creed or nationality, in whatever manner the Board of Trustees may decide.

ARTICLE IV

The principal office or place of business shall be at the City of Battle Creek in the County of Calhoun in the State of Michigan.

ARTICLE V

(a) The amount of assets which said corporation possesses is:
Real property: None
Personal property: One Thousand ($1,000) Dollars

(b) Said corporation is to be financed under the following general plan:

By receiving gifts, devices and bequests and by receiving the net income, issues, and profits of gifts, devices, bequests and trust funds.

There shall be no membership fee or dues.

Under the provisions of the above named act said corporation does not intend to issue shares of stock.

ARTICLE VI

THE term of existence of this proposed corporation is and shall be perpetual from the date of these articles.

ARTICLE VII

THE incorporating members of the association are as follows:

Names	*Residence Addresses*
A. C. SELMON, M.D.,	Stringham Road, Battle Creek, Michigan
EUGENE MCKAY,	188 Hubbard St., Battle Creek, Michigan
LEWIS J. BROWN,	Michigan Ave., W, Battle Creek, Michigan

ARTICLE VIII

THE names and addresses of the officers and directors for the first year are as follows:

Names	*Office*	*Address*
A. C. SELMON, M.D.,	*President and Director*,	Battle Creek, Michigan
EUGENE MCKAY,	*Vice President and Director*,	Battle Creek, Michigan
LEWIS J. BROWN,	*Secretary-Treasurer and Director*,	Battle Creek, Michigan

Provided, that from and after August 31st, 1934, the property and business of this corporation shall be held and managed by a Board of Trustees. The number (not less than three nor more than fifteen), the qualifications, classification, term of office, manner of election, manner of removal, time and place of meeting, and the powers, authorities, and duties of the Trustees, subject to the provisions of all applicable statutes, shall be prescribed by the By-Laws of this corporation duly adopted from time to time. The word "Trustees" as used herein shall be deemed synonymous with the word "Directors."

ARTICLE IX

THE terms on and manner in which members may be admitted to this corporation and in which membership therein shall be retained or terminated shall be as follows:

Section 1. The corporation shall have a total of nine members.

Section 2. The members of the corporation shall consist of Stuart Pritchard, M.D., Eugene McKay, Mrs. Bessie Rogers, John L. Kellogg, Jr., Fred Sherriff, Glenn A. Cross, and Henry F. Vaughan, the present members of this corporation, and such additional persons as shall be elected to membership from time to time in accordance with these Articles.

Each of the present members of this corporation shall remain a member for the term for which he shall be elected as hereinafter set forth, unless his membership shall be terminated in accordance with these Articles. Each member hereafter elected (including present members, if subsequently elected to membership) shall remain a member for the term for which he shall have been elected, unless his membership shall be terminated, in accordance with these Articles.

Section 3. The members at all times shall be divided into three classes, equal numerically as nearly as may be, and they shall be so arranged that the membership of one class shall expire at the conclusion of the annual meeting of the members of this corporation to be held in the year 1935; and of the second class at the conclusion of the annual meeting of the members of this corporation to be held in the year 1936; and of the third class at the conclusion of the annual meeting of the members of this corporation to be held in the year 1937.

For the purpose of making the division of the membership into such three classes, immediately after the adoption of these amendments and at the same meeting of the members at which these amendments are adopted, without further notice, Eugene McKay, the only remaining life member of this corporation, shall resign as such life member and the remaining six of the present members of this corporation shall elect three additional members of this corporation so as to complete the membership in this corporation to the total of nine and thereupon make division of the total membership, by election, into three classes who shall be elected to membership for the terms hereinbefore specified.

At the annual meeting of the members of this corporation to be held in the year 1935 and in each year thereafter, or at any adjournment thereof, three members shall be elected to membership, as successors to the three members whose term of membership expires in that year.

Section 4. A member may be elected to membership to succeed himself. Members whose terms of office expire at the conclusion of a meeting may vote at that meeting upon all matters coming before the meeting, including elections to membership and elections to membership in the Board of Trustees. A member's membership shall continue, notwithstanding the expiration of the term of office for which he was elected, until the conclusion of the meeting at which his successor shall be elected. In case of resignation or removal of a member, however, his resignation or removal, *ipso facto*, shall determine his membership.

Section 5. In case of any vacancy in the membership occurring, whether caused by death, resignation, removal, or otherwise, the vacancy shall be filled by election of a new member for the unexpired term of the member so dying, resigning or removed, at an annual or special meeting of the members.

Section 6. All members shall be elected to membership in the manner herein provided.

Section 7. At any meeting of the members a quorum shall consist of a majority of the members of this corporation at the time. No member shall be permitted to vote by proxy at a membership meeting. No person shall be elected to membership who does not receive the votes of at least five members, provided that in case the membership shall be reduced to six or less, members may be elected by the votes of two-thirds of the total number of members of this corporation at the time.

Section 8. Not more than four (4) members of this corporation may be officers or employees of this corporation devoting their full time to the affairs of this corporation for a remuneration, but nothing herein shall be construed to prevent payment to officers, members or trustees of any compensation provided for their benefit in any will, trust, or other instrument under which this corporation may receive funds. A trustee shall not be considered to be within the prohibition contained in this section, merely because he may receive compensation under the By-Laws for his services in attending meetings of the Board of Trustees. A trustee, officer, or employee shall not be considered to be within the prohibition contained in this section because he renders part-time service to this corporation for which he receives compensation if he does not devote his full working time to the service of this corporation for a remuneration paid to him.

Section 9. Any member may withdraw from this corporation by resignation filed with the Secretary. His resignation shall become effective upon its filing.

Section 10. The members of the corporation, by a majority vote at an annual or a special meeting may remove any member for conduct deemed by the members of the corporation to be injurious to the standing, credit or the affairs of this corporation, provided in such case the member first shall be personally served with the charges, in written form, brought against him, and shall be given a fair opportunity to be heard before the members of the corporation in his own defense.

Section 11. No act of the corporation or of the Board of Trustees shall be void because at the time such act shall be done the members or trustees of the corporation shall be less in number than that prescribed by the Articles of Incorporation or the By-Laws of this corporation.

Section 12. Each present and every future member of this corporation, by acceptance of membership in this corporation, renounces, and shall be construed to have renounced, for himself, his heirs, legatees, devisees, legal representatives and assigns, each, any and every right under any present or future law to participate to any extent whatsoever in the assets of this corporation upon liquidation, winding up or dissolution, and in case this corporation shall cease to operate, or shall divert its funds from the lawful purposes of its organization, or become unable to usefully serve such purposes, any court of equity of competent jurisdiction shall have the right to appoint trustees to carry on the purposes of this corporation and to administer its assets until the legislature shall by law make the provision authorized in Section 167 of Act Number 327 of the Public Acts of Michigan of 1931.

ARTICLE X

All present and future members of this corporation hereby consent and agree that they will not cause these Articles of Association to be amended except (a) by compliance with all of the provisions of law relating to amendments, and (b) in addition thereto by adding to the certificate of amendment (or other instrument required by law for affecting such amendment) filed in the office of the Secretary of State of the State of Michigan, or in the office of such other officer as may be designated by law, a full statement of the reason or reasons pursuant to which such amendment is made, which reasons shall be spread at length upon the records of the meeting at which such amendment was adopted.

IN WITNESS WHEREOF, We, the parties associating as shown under Article VII of these articles, for the purpose of giving legal effect to these articles, hereunto sign our names this 19th day of June, A.D. 1930.

A. C. Selmon
Eugene H. McKay
Lewis J. Brown

State of Michigan
} ss.
County of Calhoun

On this 19th day of June, A.D., 1930, before me, a Notary Public in and for said County personally appeared A. C. Selmon, Eugene H. McKay, and Lewis J. Brown known to me to be the persons named in, and who executed the foregoing instrument, and severally acknowledged that they executed the same freely and for the intents and purposes therein mentioned.

Theresa F. Gibbons
(Seal) Notary Public.
My commission expires Dec. 3, 1933.

Appendix C

BY-LAWS

OF THE W. K. KELLOGG FOUNDATION

(As of November 17, 1941)

ARTICLE I

MEETINGS OF THE MEMBERS OF THE CORPORATION

Section 1. (a) The Annual Meeting of the members of the corporation shall be held at the principal office of the W. K. Kellogg Foundation, in Battle Creek, Michigan, or at such other place as may be designated by the Board of Trustees, at 11:00 o'clock, A.M., Eastern Standard Time, on the third Tuesday of November in each year. If that day shall be a legal holiday in any year, the meeting shall be held at the same place at the same time on the next following business day.

(b) At the annual meeting of the corporation, the President and General Director shall present a joint written report for the last fiscal year, and the Treasurer also shall present a separate written report for the last fiscal year. The President and General Director's report shall contain a summary of the operations of the corporation for the last fiscal year and a summary of the plans of the corporation adopted or in contemplation for the then fiscal year. The Treasurer's report shall contain a summary of the assets of the corporation at the end of the last fiscal year, including assets owned by the corporation in its own right and those held in trust by or for it, a summary of the important acquisitions and dispositions of assets occurring during the last fiscal year, a summary of the receipts and the disbursements and of the appropriations made and expended for that year, and a summary of the liabilities, direct and contingent, of the corporation at the end of the last fiscal year.

Section 2. Special Meetings of the members may be called by resolution of the Board of Trustees, or by the Chairman of the Board of Trustees, the President, or one-third of the members of the corporation at the time. Unless made at the direction of the Board of Trustees, the call shall be in writing and shall state the day, hour and object or objects of such special meeting, and the call shall be filed with the Secretary, or Assistant Secretary of the corporation at least twenty-four hours prior to the time of the meeting. Such meetings shall be held at the principal office of the corporation in Battle Creek, Michigan, or at such other place as may be designated by the Board of Trustees, or the Chairman of the Board of Trustees, or the President.

Section 3. (a) Notices of Members Meetings. The notice of the annual meeting of the members shall be mailed by the Secretary of the corporation to the last known post office address of each member, not less than five days before any such meeting.

(b) Notice of any special meeting of the members shall be given to each member, either by the Secretary of the corporation, or by the person or persons calling such meeting, by depositing such notice at least twenty-four hours before such meeting in the United States mail, postage prepaid, or by sending a prepaid telegram, cablegram, or radiogram, addressed in any case to the member at his last known post office address.

(c) The notice of any annual or special meeting of the members shall state the place, day and hour thereof. At any annual meeting, or adjournment thereof, any business of the corporation may be transacted without any specification of its character in the notice of the meeting. The notice of any special meeting shall briefly state the object or objects thereof, and also the place, day and hour thereof. No notice need be given of any adjourned session of any regular or special meeting, other than the announcement made at the meeting of the time and place of holding the adjourned session.

(d) A call for or a notice of any meeting of the members of the corporation may be waived by any member, by telegram, radiogram, cablegram, or other writing. Such waiver may be made either before or after the holding of the meeting. Any meeting of the members shall be a legal meeting without call therefor having been made, or any notice thereof having been given, if the members either shall be present thereat or shall give consent in writing to the holding of the meeting.

(e) No failure to give notice, nor any irregularity in the notice of any meeting shall invalidate such meeting or any proceeding thereat.

Section 4. A QUORUM at any meeting of the members shall consist of a majority of the members of the corporation at the time. Except as provided in the Articles of Association or by statute, no resolution shall be passed or action taken by the members, other than adjournment, unless at least five members shall vote in the affirmative therefor, but if the members shall be reduced to six or less, the votes of two-thirds of the members at the time, in the affirmative, may decide any question or elect any member or elect to membership in the Board of Trustees. Each member of the corporation shall be entitled to one vote on all questions coming before a meeting. In the absence of a quorum those present may adjourn the meeting to a future date, at which time, if a quorum is present, any action may be taken which might have been taken at the meeting as originally called.

Section 5. The PRESIDING OFFICER at meetings of the members shall be the Chairman of the Board of Trustees if he desires to so preside. When the Chairman of the Board of Trustees is absent, or being present does not desire to act as presiding officer, the President shall preside, or the next officer in due order who may be present. The due order for the purposes of these By-Laws shall be Chairman of the Board of Trustees, President, Vice-President, Treasurer, Secretary.

Section 6. HONORARY TRUSTEES may be elected from among non-members of this corporation, at any annual or special meeting of the members or adjournment thereof. They shall hold office, when elected, until the conclusion of the next annual meeting of the members of the corporation. Their powers and duties are provided in clause (i) of Section 1, Article II, of these By-Laws.

Section 7. The ORDER OF BUSINESS at the annual meeting and as far as possible at all other meetings of the members shall be:

1. Roll call.
2. Proof of due notice of meeting.
3. Reading and disposal of any unapproved minutes.
4. Annual reports of officers.
5. Unfinished business.
6. Elections to membership in this corporation.
7. Elections of Trustees.
8. Elections of Honorary Trustees.
9. New business.
10. Adjournment.

ARTICLE II

BOARD OF TRUSTEES AND MEETINGS OF THE BOARD

Section 1. (a) The property and business of this corporation shall be held and managed by a board of nine trustees. The Board of Trustees shall possess and exercise all of the powers and authority of this corporation, and all such powers and authority as shall be necessary to the complete execution of the purposes of this corporation, except as limited by its Articles of Association or by these By-Laws.

(b) The Board of Trustees shall be divided into three equal classes, and these classes shall be so arranged that the term of office of one class shall expire at the conclusion of each annual meeting of the members of the corporation. At each annual meeting of the members of the corporation hereafter to be held or at an adjournment thereof, three trustees shall be elected who shall hold office until the conclusion of the annual meeting of the members to be held in the third year following their election.

(c) Each trustee shall continue in office until his successor shall have been elected and qualified, except in the case of trustees who resign or are removed. Resignation or removal of a trustee shall immediately terminate his membership in the Board of Trustees.

(d) In the case of all elections of trustees by members of the corporation where there are a greater number of candidates than the number to be elected, each trustee shall be separately elected. Each trustee elected shall receive the affirmative votes of at least five members of the corporation, unless the number of members of the corporation shall be reduced to six or less, in which case he shall receive the votes of at least two-thirds of the total number of the members of the corporation at the time.

(e) All trustees shall be elected from among the members of the corporation. The termination of any trustee's membership in the corporation shall disqualify him from continuing to further act as a trustee and shall constitute a removal from his office of trustee.

(f) The members of the corporation by majority vote at an annual or a special meeting may remove any trustee for conduct deemed injurious to the standing, credit or affairs of the corporation, or for unexcused failure of the trustee to attend meetings of the Board of Trustees during a period of three consecutive months, provided the trustee shall first be personally served with the charges, in written form brought against him, and shall be given a fair opportunity to be heard before the members of the corporation in his own defense.

(g) Whenever a vacancy shall occur in the Board of Trustees, by death, resignation or removal, a trustee shall be appointed by the remaining trustees. Such appointee shall hold office until the next annual meeting of the members of the corporation, at which meeting the members of the corporation shall elect a trustee to fill the vacancy for the unexpired term.

(h) Nothing herein shall prevent a trustee from being re-elected to succeed himself.

(i) An honorary trustee may attend meetings of the Board of Trustees, on invitation of the presiding officer. He shall not be entitled to vote, but may enter into all discussions at any meeting of the Board of Trustees to which he is invited. An honorary trustee shall not have power to bind the corporation in any manner.

(j) Each trustee shall receive a reasonable compensation and reasonable expenses for each meeting of the Board of Trustees he shall attend. The amount of such compensation shall be fixed from time to time by action of the Board of Trustees; provided the trustees acting under the W. K. Kellogg Foundation Trust, also known as Trust 5315 of Harris Trust and Savings Bank, shall approve and certify that the compensation so fixed, together with reimbursement for expenses, is reasonable. At the discretion of the Board of Trustees, an honorary trustee shall receive reasonable compensation and reasonable expenses for each meeting of the Board of Trustees he shall attend on invitation of the presiding officer. The amount of such compensation shall be fixed from time to time by action of the Board of Trustees.

Section 2. REGULAR MEETINGS of the Board of Trustees shall be held at the principal office of the W. K. Kellogg Foundation, in Battle Creek, Michigan, or at such other place as may be designated by the Board of Trustees, or by the Chairman of the Board of Trustees, or by the President of the corporation. Such meetings shall be held on the third Tuesday of each month (if not a legal holiday, but if a legal holiday then on the next business day following) at the hour of 11:00 A.M., Eastern Standard Time. At least one meeting of the Board of Trustees, regular or special, shall be held in Battle Creek, Michigan, in each month.

Section 3. SPECIAL MEETINGS of the Board of Trustees shall be held at the principal office of the W. K. Kellogg Foundation, in Battle Creek, Michigan, or at such other place as may be designated by the Board of Trustees, or by the Chairman of the Board of Trustees, or by the President of the corporation. Such meetings shall be held at any time provided in a resolution adopted by the Board of Trustees, or in a call for a special meeting made by the Chairman of the Board of Trustees, or by the President, or by three members of the Board, or shall be held at any time and place without notice, if the trustees are present, or if those not present shall give their written consent to the holding of the meeting. Any call for a special meeting which shall be made otherwise than by resolution adopted by the Board of Trustees shall be in writing, shall state the object or objects of such meeting, and shall be filed with the Secretary or Assistant Secretary of the corporation at least twenty-four hours prior to the time of the meeting.

Section 4. (a) NOTICE of any regular meeting of the Board of Trustees shall be mailed by the Secretary of the corporation to the last known post office address of each trustee not less than five days before the meeting.

(b) Notice of any special meeting of the Board of Trustees shall be given to each trustee, either by the Secretary of the corporation, or by the person or persons calling the meeting by depositing such notice at least twenty-four hours before such meeting in the United States mail, postage prepaid, or by sending a prepaid telegram, cablegram, or radiogram, addressed in any case to the trustee at his last known post office address.

(c) The notice of any regular or special meeting of the Board shall state the place, day, and hour thereof. At any regular meeting, or adjournment thereof, any business of the corporation may be transacted without any specification of its character in the notice of the meeting. The notice of any special meeting shall briefly state the object or objects thereof and also the place, day and hour thereof.

(d) A call for or a notice of any meeting of the Board of Trustees may be waived by any trustee, by telegram, radiogram, cablegram, or other writing. Such waiver may be made either before or after the holding of the meeting. Any meeting of the Board of Trustees shall be a legal meeting without call therefor having been made, or any notice thereof having been given, if the trustees either shall be present thereat or shall give consent in writing to the holding of the meeting.

(e) No notice need be given of any adjourned session of any regular or special meeting of the Board other than the announcement made at the meeting of the time and place of holding the adjourned session.

(f) No failure to give notice nor any irregularity in the notice of any meeting of the Board shall invalidate such meeting or any proceedings thereat.

Section 5. A QUORUM at any meeting of the Board of Trustees shall consist of a majority of the Board at the time. Except as provided in the Articles of Association, the statutes, or these By-Laws, no resolution shall be passed or action taken by the Board, other than adjournment, unless at least five trustees shall vote in the affirmative therefor, but if the number of trustees shall be reduced to six or less the votes in the affirmative of two-thirds of the trustees at the time may decide any question. In the absence of a quorum those present may adjourn the meeting to a future date at which time, if a quorum is present, any action may be taken which might have been taken at the meeting as originally called.

Section 6. The ORDER OF BUSINESS at any regular or special meeting of the Board of Trustees, unless otherwise prescribed for any meeting of the Board, shall be as follows:

1. Roll Call.
2. Reading and disposal of any unapproved minutes.
3. Reports of officers and committees.
4. Unfinished business.
5. Election of officers.
6. New business.
7. Adjournment.

ARTICLE III

OFFICERS

Section 1. (a) The OFFICERS of the corporation shall be a President, Vice-President, General Director, Secretary, Treasurer, and Comptroller. The Board of Trustees also may elect a Chairman of the Board, an Assistant Secretary, and an Assistant Treasurer. The Board of Trustees may also elect assistants to any of the aforesaid officers and prescribe the powers and duties of such assistants.

(b) Any two or more offices of the Foundation may be held by one person.

(c) The President, Vice-President, and General Director shall be members of the corporation and members of the Board of Trustees. No other officer need be a member of the corporation or a member of the Board of Trustees.

Section 2. The CHAIRMAN OF THE BOARD OF TRUSTEES shall sustain an advisory relation to the work and policies of the corporation. If the Chairman of the Board so desires, he shall preside at all meetings of the members and of the Board of Trustees at which he shall be present. He shall have the right to attend any meeting of any board, or other agency of the corporation, and the provisions of the By-Laws with reference to notice of such meetings and of the business to be transacted thereat shall be deemed to include him, but he shall be under no obligation to attend. He shall not be counted to determine the number necessary to make a quorum or to determine whether a quorum is present at any meeting of the members or the Board of Trustees, unless he is a member or trustee, as the case may be. He shall have no vote at any meeting at which he is in attendance, by virtue of his office as Chairman of the Board of Trustees, but he shall not by reason of that office be disqualified from voting if otherwise qualified.

Section 3. The PRESIDENT shall sign or counter-sign all contracts and other instruments of the corporation authorized by the Board of Trustees, except as otherwise directed by the Board, shall preside over all meetings of the Board of Trustees and members of the corporation, in the absence of the Chairman of the Board of Trustees, or when the Chairman of the Board of Trustees does not desire to act as the presiding officer, and shall make such reports to the trustees and members of the corporation as he may deem necessary, or which are required by these By-Laws, or which may be required of him by the Board of Trustees, and perform such other duties and exercise such other powers as may be imposed upon him from time to time by the Board of Trustees. He shall jointly with the General Director supervise and manage the business and affairs of the corporation with such division of responsibility, not otherwise determined by these By-Laws, as may be from time to time agreed upon by these two officers. He shall be a member, ex officio, of any committee of officers or employees or of any technical advisory board or boards created under the provisions of these By-Laws. He shall nominate to the Board of Trustees and to the members of the corporation candidates for all elective or appointive offices unless otherwise provided in the Articles of Association or the By-Laws or ordered by the members, or the Board of Trustees, but his duty to nominate shall not be construed to prevent any other person qualified from submitting nominations.

Section 4. The VICE-PRESIDENT, in the absence or disability of the President, shall exercise all of the powers and perform all of the duties of the President. He shall also perform all other duties imposed upon him by the Board of Trustees. The Vice-President shall also exercise any of the functions of the President which the President may request.

Section 5. The GENERAL DIRECTOR shall execute the policies and program adopted by the Board of Trustees from time to time. He shall jointly with the President supervise and manage the business and affairs of the corporation with such division of responsibility, not otherwise determined by these By-Laws, as may be from time to time agreed upon by these two officers. He shall be a member ex officio of any committee of officers or employees or of any technical advisory board or boards created under the provisions of these By-Laws. He shall have power to employ, remove, and suspend all agents or members of the corporation not elected or appointed by the Board of Trustees; to determine and change their duties from time to time; to fix and change their compensation; to require security of them; to create such titles for such positions filled by his authority as may be regarded as desirable to enable the appointees to execute the duties and responsibilities, and to do all other things not expressly provided for and prohibited by these By-Laws, necessary or proper, in his opinion to accomplish any of the objectives, or effectively exercise any powers specified in this Section. In the absence or disability of the General Director, the powers and duties of the General Director or any of them, may be exercised and performed by the President, except as the Board of Trustees from time to time may otherwise direct.

Section 6. The SECRETARY shall issue notices for all meetings of the members of the corporation and the Board of Trustees, and shall keep in books belonging to the corporation the minutes of the meetings of the members of the corporation, and of its Board of Trustees, and the Secretary shall have charge of the Seal and the corporate minute books, shall sign with the President instruments requiring his signature, and shall make such reports and perform such other duties as are incident to his office, or are required by these By-Laws, or which may be required of him by the Board of Trustees.

Section 7. The TREASURER shall have the custody of all moneys of the corporation and shall keep the general books of account of the corporation and balance the same each month. The Treasurer shall have the custody of all securities of the corporation and be responsible for their safe-keeping, unless by resolution of the Board of Trustees a securities committee, securities custodian or other agency shall be appointed to have the custody of all or a portion of the securities. The Treasurer shall supervise the making of all disbursements for the purchase of securities, and shall have charge of keeping expenditures for the purchase of securities within the limits of authorizations approved by the Board of Trustees. The Treasurer shall sign or countersign such instruments requiring his signature and shall perform all duties incident to his office or which are required of him by these By-Laws, or by the Board of Trustees. The Treasurer shall give bond in such amount and with such security as shall be specified from time to time by the Trustees of the W. K. Kellogg Foundation Trust, also known as Trust 5315 of Harris Trust and Savings Bank. The Treasurer shall give additional bond or security to that which may be so required by such trustees, if directed so to do by resolution of the Board of Trustees. The bond of the Treasurer shall be conditioned for the faithful performance of his duties, and the conditions thereof, the security thereon and the amount thereof, subject to the provisions hereinabove contained, shall be approved by the Board of Trustees.

Section 8. A COMPTROLLER shall also be elected by the Board of Trustees. The Comptroller shall supervise the making of all disbursements and expenditures by the corporation, except those relating to the purchase of securities. He shall prepare its budgets, have supervision of the accounting procedure and the preparation of adequate records and data with regard to its commitments and expenditures other than those relating to the purchase of securities, and have general charge of keeping expenditures and commitments of the corporation not relating to the purchase of securities within authorizations approved by the Board of Trustees. He shall make reports from time to time to the Board of Trustees. He shall also perform such other duties as he may be directed to perform by the Board of Trustees or the President. In the absence or disability of the Comptroller, his powers and duties shall be exercised and performed by such officer or employee of the corporation as the President shall designate, from time to time.

Section 9. An ASSISTANT SECRETARY may also be elected by the Board of Trustees. The Assistant Secretary shall perform the same duties and exercise the same powers as the Secretary, and perform such other duties as he may be directed to perform by the Board of Trustees or the President.

Section 10. An ASSISTANT TREASURER may also be elected by the Board of Trustees. The Assistant Treasurer shall perform the same duties and exercise the same powers as the Treasurer, except that the Assistant Treasurer shall not have custody of the moneys or securities of the corporation, unless he shall be appointed a member of a Securities Committee, although he may be authorized to sign or counter-sign checks in the name of the corporation drawn upon any account in any bank in which the corporation has funds on deposit. The Assistant Treasurer also shall perform such other duties as he may be directed to perform by the Board of Trustees or the President.

Section 11. OFFICERS OF THE CORPORATION shall be elected by the Board of Trustees at their first meeting following the annual meeting of the members of the corporation or as soon thereafter as practicable. All officers of the corporation shall be elected for a term expiring at the conclusion of the first meeting of the Board of Trustees following the next annual meeting of the members of the corporation. Each officer shall hold his office until his successor is elected and qualified, except an officer resigning or being removed. If any office becomes vacant, the Board of Trustees shall fill the same for the unexpired term. Any officer of the corporation may be removed by the Board of Trustees, for or without cause, by resolution adopted by the affirmative votes of at least five members of the Board, or in case there shall only be six or a lesser number of trustees in office at the time, then by resolution adopted by the affirmative votes of two-thirds of all the trustees then in office.

Section 12. The Board of Trustees by resolution may provide for the creation of one or more TECHNICAL ADVISORY BOARDS consisting of such number of technical advisors as the Board may deem expedient, to be appointed by the General Director, and the Board of Trustees may define the scope and functions of such boards but no such board shall have power to bind the corporation. The Board of Trustees may provide for compensation to be paid to members of the technical advisory boards and make allowances to them for travel expenses. If any technical advisory board is appointed, the General Director shall have power to call meetings of such Board and fix the time and place of the meetings and the notice to be given thereof. Those present at a meeting of a technical advisory board shall constitute a quorum. Each such board shall elect its chairman and secretary and it shall keep records of its meetings and actions and such records at all times shall be open for inspection of the General Director and any trustee.

Section 13. The General Director shall have power in his discretion to create any COMMITTEE or COMMITTEES of officers or employees of the corporation, with such titles as he may designate, for the purpose of consulting and advising with him on any matters concerning the affairs of the corporation. There shall be no necessity of keeping a record of the proceedings of any such committee unless the General Director requires records to be kept.

Section 14. Any officer or agent or the corporation may be required to give BOND for the faithful performance of his duties in such sum and in such form, and with such surety thereon, as the Board of Trustees shall decide.

ARTICLE IV

FINANCE

Section 1. SECURITIES COMMITTEE. The Board of Trustees, from time to time, may appoint a Securities Committee to have custody of any class or classes of securities, or of any specified securities, of the corporation. Such committee shall consist of not less than three persons. It shall be the duty of such committee to keep the securities belonging to the corporation entrusted to its custody in such vault or vaults as may be designated by the Board of Trustees, but such vault may be a compartment in the safe of the corporation kept in its principal office. Access to such vaults shall be had by not less than two members of such committee. The Board of Trustees may remove one or more members of such Securities Committee at any time and appoint others in the places of those removed, or fill any vacancies in the committee that may at any time exist, or abolish the committee. Such committee need not be made up of members or officers of the corporation. To the extent that a Securities Committee is appointed to have custody of any specified class or classes of securities, or any specified securities, the Treasurer shall be relieved of all responsibility for the custody thereof.

Section 2. CUSTODIAN OF SECURITIES. The Board of Trustees, from time to time, may appoint one or more banks or trust companies doing business in Michigan or elsewhere, to act for a reasonable compensation as custodian of any designated class or classes of securities or of any particularly described securities of the corporation, and to exercise in respect thereof such powers as may be conferred by resolution of the Board of Trustees. The Board of Trustees may remove any such custodian at any time. The Treasurer shall be relieved of all responsibility for any securities committed by the Board of Trustees to the custody of any such securities custodian.

Section 3. FINANCE COMMITTEE. (a) The Board of Trustees shall appoint a Finance Committee composed of four members of the Board. The Board of Trustees shall designate one of the members of such Finance Committee to be the chairman and another to be the secretary thereof. The Board of Trustees may remove one or more members of such Finance Committee at any time, and may appoint others in place of those removed, and may fill any vacancies that may exist at any time.

(b) The President, whenever he deems it necessary, also may appoint, from time to time, a member of the Board of Trustees, to be an alternate member of the Finance Committee to serve temporarily in place of any member thereof, for such period of time as may be designated by him, and such alternate member during that period shall possess the office and powers and perform the duties of the regularly appointed member whose place he shall temporarily fill.

(c) The Finance Committee, from time to time, may purchase securities for the corporation or subscribe for the purchase of securities for the corporation, within the limits of any unexpended appropriation of funds made for that purpose by the Board of Trustees, and subject to compliance with any conditions imposed, from time to time, by the Board. Unless otherwise authorized by the Board of Trustees, the Finance Committee shall confine its purchases of securities to bonds considered by it to be of high grade, but it shall not be restricted to the purchase of bonds of such character as are or may be prescribed by law for trustees of trust estates. The Board of Trustees, however, may authorize the Finance Committee, either generally or specially, to purchase other investments, including corporate stocks of any description. The Finance Committee may sell securities, of the corporation, subject to the limitation that sales of securities exceeding $250,000 in any calendar month shall not be made by the Finance Committee unless the written approval of at least five members of the Board of Trustees to sales exceeding that amount shall be procured, but the members of the Finance Committee may be members of the Board approving of such excess sales. Any limitation contained herein upon the powers of the Finance Committee may be amended, changed or waived by the Board of Trustees either for a limited or an unlimited period of time. The Committee at each regular meeting of the Board of Trustees shall submit a written report, in such form as may be requested by the Board, of all transactions made by it during the preceding calendar month.

(d) The Finance Committee, at the expense of the corporation, may employ one or more banks or trust companies, statistical services, investment counselors, or other investment advisors to render continuous advisory investment services and to recommend such purchases and sales of securities as appear to be desirable to safeguard the interests of the corporation. In addition, it shall be the duty of the Finance Committee to present to the Board of Trustees not less frequently than semi-annually, an analysis of all securities of the corporation, which analysis, however, may be made, in whole or in part, by any agency employed by the Finance Committee.

(e) The Board of Trustees also may provide, from time to time, for the purchase or sale of any securities by any officer of the corporation or any other agency designated by it. The Board of Trustees may confer additional powers upon the Finance Committee or withdraw from it powers hereby conferred upon it.

(f) It shall not be necessary for the Finance Committee to hold meetings or to keep a formal record of its proceedings, but at least two members of such committee shall approve in writing every transaction undertaken by such committee on behalf of the corporation. Such committee shall have power to act by any two of its members, without any requirement of notice to or participation in the transaction by the other members of the committee, although it is expected that notice of any proposed transaction will be given to all members of the committee if it is practicable to do so under existing circumstances. The written approvals above required may be in the form of concurrent instruments. The record of such written approvals shall be kept by the secretary of the committee.

Section 4. BORROWING POWERS. The corporation is hereby authorized, whenever its general interests, in the opinion of the Board of Trustees require the same, or where its interests will be benefited thereby, to borrow money from time to time and issue its promissory note or notes or bond or bonds for the repayment thereof, with or without interest. The corporation is authorized whenever, in the opinion of the Board of Trustees, its general interests require the same or it will be benefited thereby, to mortgage or pledge any or all of its property or assets as security for all or any of its debts or any other lawful engagements. The Board of Trustees shall have full power to determine the particular sums of money to be borrowed from time to time, the dates when any notes or bonds given to evidence the same shall mature, the rates of interest to be paid thereon, and the nature, terms, covenants, and conditions of any mortgages or pledges of any property or assets of the corporation to be given as security.

Section 5. EXECUTION OF INSTRUMENTS. All conveyances, contracts, and mortgages shall be signed by the President and Secretary, except as otherwise provided in these By-Laws. In case of the absence or disability of the President, the Vice-President may sign in his stead. In case of the absence or disability of the Secretary, the Assistant Secretary may sign in his stead. The Board of Trustees shall have power to designate other officers or agents to execute any designated instrument.

Section 6. BANKS AND CHECKS. The moneys of the corporation shall be deposited in such manner as the Board of Trustees shall designate, in such banks or trust companies as the Board of Trustees shall direct and shall be drawn out only by checks signed in such manner as may be provided by resolution or resolutions adopted by the Board of Trustees.

Section 7. TRANSFER OF SECURITIES. The President, the Treasurer and the Chairman of the Finance Committee, or any one or more of them, shall have authority on behalf of the corporation to execute, under seal or otherwise, such transfers or assignments as may be customary or proper to constitute a regular transfer of any stocks, bonds, or other securities standing in the name of the corporation, which shall be sold, exchanged, or disposed of pursuant to authority of the Board of Trustees, general or special, or by the Finance Committee pursuant to these By-Laws or any authorization of the Board of Trustees, general or special, and any person or corporation transferring any such stocks, bonds, or other securities pursuant to a transfer or assignment executed by one of the officers above mentioned, or any one accepting any such transfer or assignment in good faith for a valuable consideration, shall be fully protected and shall have no duty to inquire whether or not the Board of Trustees or Finance Committee has taken action with respect thereto.

Section 8. Proxies. The President and the Treasurer, or either of them (unless, in any specific instance or with regard to the stock of any designated corporation or corporations, it shall be otherwise ordered by the Board of Trustees), may execute and deliver on behalf of the corporation, proxies appointing any person or persons whom he or they shall deem proper to represent and vote any stock owned or held by this corporation, at any and all meetings of the stockholders and to give consent to the creation of any mortgage, lien, or indebtedness by the corporation whose stock is so owned or held, or to a sale of all or any part of its assets, or consent to any consolidation, merger, or reorganization, with full power to alter and rescind such appointments at such times and as often as he or they shall see fit.

Section 9. Disbursements. (a) No disbursement shall be made for work upon, or for services rendered in connection with any project or program adopted by the corporation, or which it is sponsoring or executing, except pursuant to an appropriation made in an annual or supplementary budget approved by the Board of Trustees, or pursuant to a resolution of the Board of Trustees generally or specially authorizing the expenditure.

(b) No disbursement shall be made for the purchase of securities unless (1) the specific securities have been directed by the Board of Trustees to be purchased, or the purchase thereof shall have been approved by the Board of Trustees or (2) an unexpended appropriation made by the Board of Trustees for the purchase of securities exists which is equal to or in excess of the disbursement, and the disbursement is to be made pursuant thereto.

(c) No other disbursement shall be made without prior approval of the Board of Trustees, except such disbursements as are made in payment of obligations (1) incurred by the corporation in protecting, managing, or conserving its assets, or (2) properly incurred under the direction of an officer of the corporation within the scope of his powers conferred by the By-Laws or by resolution of the Board of Trustees. There shall be submitted to the Board of Trustees at each regular meeting a list of the disbursements made in the preceding calendar month for the payment of which no appropriation or prior resolution of the Board of Trustees exists.

Section 10. An Annual Audit shall be made of the financial records of the corporation, by a disinterested auditor or firm of auditors approved by the Trustees of the W. K. Kellogg Foundation Trust, also known as Trust No. 5315 of the Harris Trust and Savings Bank.

ARTICLE V

GENERAL PROVISIONS

Section 1. The Fiscal Year of the corporation shall end on the thirty-first day of August of each year, or on such other day as may be fixed from time to time by the Board of Trustees.

Section 2. The Corporate Seal of the corporation shall consist of two concentric circles between which is the name of the corporation; and in the center shall be inscribed "Corporate Seal" and such seal, as impressed on the margin hereof, shall be the Seal of the Corporation.

Section 3. VOTING BY BALLOT. At any meeting of the members, or of the Board of Trustees, upon motion duly made and carried by a majority of those entitled to vote, the voting upon any matter or question shall be by ballot.

Section 4. CHAIRMAN VOTING. At any meeting of the members, or the Board of Trustees, the chairman conducting the meeting, regardless of his title, if otherwise entitled to vote because of his being a member of the corporation or a member of the Board of Trustees, as the case may be, shall have the right to vote in the same manner as though he were not acting as chairman of the meeting.

Section 5. RESIGNATION. Any officer or trustee may resign by delivering his resignation to the Secretary of the corporation. Such resignation shall take effect from the time of its receipt by the Secretary, unless some other time is fixed in the resignation and then from that time. The acceptance of a resignation shall not be required in order to make it effective.

Section 6. DEFINITIONS. The term "Board" wherever used in these By-Laws shall be deemed to refer to the Board of Trustees, except where the context clearly indicates a different meaning. The term "corporation" wherever used shall be deemed to refer to W. K. Kellogg Foundation, except where the context clearly indicates a different meaning.

ARTICLE VI

AMENDMENTS AND REPEAL

Section 1. All former By-Laws of W. K. Kellogg Foundation and amendments thereof are hereby repealed and these By-Laws shall become effective immediately upon their adoption.

Section 2. These By-Laws may be amended, repealed, or altered, in whole or in part, at any regular meeting of the members of the corporation, or at any special meeting of the members, where such proposed action has been duly announced in the notice, or in the consent, if the meeting is held upon written consent of the members; provided that a majority of the members of the corporation at the time shall vote for such an amendment, repeal, or alteration.

Appendix D

THE CHILDREN'S CHARTER

President Hoover's White House Conference on Child Health and Protection Recognizing the Rights of the Child as the First Rights of Citizenship Pledges Itself to these Aims for the Children of America

I. For every child spiritual and moral training to help him to stand firm under the pressure of life

II. For every child understanding and the guarding of his personality as his most precious right

III. For every child a home and that love and security which a home provides; and for that child who must receive foster care, the nearest substitute for his own home

IV. For every child full preparation for his birth, his mother receiving prenatal, natal, and postnatal care; and the establishment of such protective measures as will make child-bearing safer

V. For every child health protection from birth through adolescence, including: periodical health examinations and, where needed, care of specialists and hospital treatment; regular dental examination and care of the teeth; protective and preventive measures against communicable diseases; the insuring of pure food, pure milk, and pure water

VI. For every child from birth through adolescence, promotion of health, including health instruction and a health program, wholesome physical and mental recreation, with teachers and leaders adequately trained

VII. For every child a dwelling place safe, sanitary, and wholesome, with reasonable provisions for privacy, free from conditions which tend to thwart his development; and a home environment harmonious and enriching

VIII. For every child a school which is safe from hazards, sanitary, properly equipped, lighted, and ventilated. For younger children nursery schools and kindergartens to supplement home care

IX. For every child a community which recognizes and plans for his needs, protects him against physical dangers, moral hazards, and disease; provides him with safe and wholesome places for play and recreation; and makes provision for his cultural and social needs

X. For every child an education which, through the discovery and development of his individual abilities, prepares him for life; and through training and vocational guidance prepares him for a living which will yield him the maximum of satisfaction

XI. For every child such teaching and training as will prepare him for successful parenthood, homemaking, and the rights of citizenship; and, for parents, supplementary training to fit them to deal wisely with the problems of parenthood

XII. For every child education for safety and protection against accidents to which modern conditions subject him—those to which he is directly exposed and those which, through loss or maiming of his parents, affect him indirectly

XIII. For every child who is blind, deaf, crippled, or otherwise physically handicapped, and for the child who is mentally handicapped, such measures as will early discover and diagnose his handicap, provide care and treatment, and so train him that he may become an asset to society rather than a liability. Expenses of these services should be borne publicly where they cannot be privately met

XIV. For every child who is in conflict with society the right to be dealt with intelligently as society's charge, not society's outcast; with the home, the school, the church, the court and the institution when needed, shaped to return him whenever possible to the normal stream of life

XV. For every child the right to grow up in a family with an adequate standard of living and the security of a stable income as the surest safeguard against social handicaps

XVI. For every child protection against labor that stunts growth, either physical or mental, that limits education, that deprives children of the right of comradeship, of play, and of joy

XVII. For every rural child as satisfactory schooling and health services as for the city child, and an extension to rural families of social, recreational, and cultural facilities

XVIII. To supplement the home and the school in the training of youth, and to return to them those interests of which modern life tends to cheat children, every stimulation and encouragement should be given to the extension and development of the voluntary youth organizations

XIX. To make everywhere available these minimum protections of the health and welfare of children, there should be a district, county, or community organization for health, education, and welfare, with full-time officials, coordinating with a statewide program which will be responsive to a nation-wide service of general information, statistics, and scientific research. This should include:

(a) Trained, full-time public health officials, with public health nurses, sanitary inspection, and laboratory workers

(b) Available hospital beds

(c) Full-time public welfare service for the relief, aid, and guidance of children in special need due to poverty, misfortune, or behavior difficulties, and for the protection of children from abuse, neglect, exploitation, or moral hazard

For EVERY child these rights, regardless of race, or color, or situation, wherever he may live under the protection of the American flag